WILDFLOWERS
OF WESTERN AUSTRALIA

D1324401

THIRTEENTH EDITION

△ The Christmas tree of south-western Australia *Nuytsia floribunda* (Labill.) R.Br. is remarkable because it is a parasite, yet grows independently in the ground. It flowers at Christmas with masses of brilliant blooms.

Rick

WILDFLOWERS
OF WESTERN AUSTRALIA

by
C. A. GARDNER

edited by
JACK EDMONDS

THIRTEENTH EDITION

1978
WEST AUSTRALIAN NEWSPAPERS LTD.
PERTH

WILDFLOWERS OF WESTERN AUSTRALIA

First published 1959
Thirteenth Edition 1978.
Text by C. A. Gardner, Government Botanist and Curator of the Western Australian Herbarium 1927-61; updated by R. D. Royce, Government Botanist and Herbarium Curator 1961-1974.
Edited and produced by Jack Edmonds.
Published by West Australian Newspapers Ltd., Periodicals Division, 125 St. Georges Tce., Perth, Western Australia, 6000.
Painted illustrations by Edgar Dell.
Photographs by Norman Taylor, Max Holten, Phil Martin, Tom Dann; processed in the W.A. Newspapers colour laboratory.
Colour plates etched by Norman Smith and Lee Riseley, laid down by Harold Birch.
Printed by Wescolour Press, a division of West Australian Newspapers Ltd., 340 High Street, East Fremantle, Western Australia, 6158.
Bound by Printers Trade Services, Perth.
Completely produced in Western Australia.

COPYRIGHT: All rights reserved.

National Library of Australia Card Number and International Standard Book Number 0 909699 01 1.
Library of Congress Catalog Card Number 73-80057.

Acknowledgment

MUCH painstaking work by many people has gone into this book. The text by Charles Gardner is the product of a lifetime spent studying Western Australia's plants and flowers. Edgar Dell devoted many hours painting illustrations with meticulous correctness. Norman Taylor and Max Holten also expended many hours, in the bush, to capture so skilfully with their cameras the beauty which Mr. Gardner wrote about. Norman Smith and Lee Riseley employed equal patience and skill to transfer that beauty from film to printing plate. Harold Birch and Ron Johnson laid down the plates which were printed so faithfully by Wescolour Press.

Bob Royce, as Government Botanist, cheerfully did everything that any man could do to ensure the botanical accuracy of the new edition. He and his staff at the Western Australian Herbarium positively identified 328 species from hundreds of transparencies, colour prints and specimens which were submitted to them in its preparation.

This book is a measure of the craftsmanship of all these people.

—*Jack Edmonds, Editor*

CONTENTS

Introduction

THERE are few places in the world which are so renowned—both within their own boundaries and beyond their frontiers—for a wealth of wild-flowers as Western Australia. So exceptional is the variety of the flora, indeed, that it has proved impracticable to include illustrations of more than a small proportion of the many lovely examples available.

The splendours of colour and the diversity of tint and shade have made this flora world famous, for, dull though most of the foliage may be, sometimes small, dry, brittle and unattractive, the delightful form and hues of the flowers are outstanding. We may find one genus which exhibits the whole range of colours: in *Lechenaultia,* for example, pale and rich blue, brilliant scarlet, intense crimson and a glowing yellow are to be seen. Similarly there are amazing combinations of contrasting colours, as in Kangaroo paws, when blood red and emerald green, gold and black, flame and purple are found. Vivid woolly calyces, highly coloured felted leaves—more striking than the flowers themselves—stems of a sharply opposing shade to the surrounding soil . . . all of these, too, frequently make the native plant life so arresting.

During the Western Australian winter and spring the burgeoning of this striking natural phenomenon provides an unparalleled display, yet even during the months of high summer the landscape is not without flowers. Round about May the first winter rains are enjoyed, and then some of the wattles, white heaths and sundews begin to provide splashes of loveliness, and, as the weeks pass, more and more blossoms ornament what may have been disregarded as seemingly uninteresting and often dusty growth on shrub, climber and tree, while more and more annuals thrust up little sprays or long spikes further to beautify paddock, bush and roadside. By the time October arrives a magnificent showing of flowers of all types and colours, small and large, delicate and handsome, will have delighted those fortunate enough to have seen the unequalled display in what might be a wild garden millions of acres in extent. Even after this the days of the long, hot, dry summer are brightened by vast arrays of smokebush, of *Eucalyptus* trees and shrubs in bloom, of *Verticordias* advertising their loveliness, of many kinds of *Banksia,* and of the Christmas-tree *(Nuytsia floribunda)* throwing its flaming inflorescence against the cloudless blue sky.

△ *Lechenaultia* is a genus with an ▽ extremely wide range of colours.

△ Both pale and rich blues above are *Lechenaultia biloba* Lindl.

△ *L. biloba* also has a white form.
▽ *L. formosa* R.Br., yellow or red.

▽ *Lechenaultia hirsuta* F.Muell.

▽ *Lechenaultia laricina* L.

SINCE the days of settlement of Western Australia in 1829 the plants of this great land have interested and received attention from botanists and horticulturists. Indeed, the visit of Joseph Banks (later to be knighted and to be recognised as one of the world's outstanding botanists), who accompanied Captain Cook in 1769-70, focussed attention on the then unknown continent. It was because of the representations by Banks to the British Government that Matthew Flinders, accompanied by Robert Brown, sailed in the Investigator (1801) to discover much of, and give a name to, Australia. Robert Brown, also regarded as an illustrious name in botanical history, laid the foundations for the study of systematic botany in this country.

The names of many famous botanists and explorers are commemorated in the names of plants—Sir Joseph Banks *(Banksia),* Leschenault *(Lechenaultia),* and so on; others equally well known were Labillardiere (who visited these shores in 1792 with the French expedition led by D'Entrecasteaux), Dampier, Roe, Forrest, Giles, Mueller, Drummond, Lindley, Cunningham, etc. The names of those who first described species are always appended to the botanical name: for example, the large enamelled orchid is *Elythranthera emarginata* Lindl.—the suffix being a shortened form of "Lindley". Other botanists are credited by the use of similar suffixes. (A list of these abbreviations is given on page 160). It will be noted, however, that while the generic name (e.g. *Elythranthera)* and the specific name (e.g. *emarginata)* are used in the text of this book, the authors' names (e.g. Lindl.) are added only when an illustration is titled.

THE noteworthy divergencies in Australian flora have always excited the attention of botanists, but that interest has been most specifically centred on the plants of the South West, for this area is the oldest part of the Australian land mass and, in a broad sense, the cradle of Australian plant life. The flora has no known beginning yet it is believed to have been of antarctic origin and its relatives today are to be found in the plant life of South America, South Africa, Antarctica, Madagascar and some Pacific islands, but such relationship is limited, for some groups are strictly confined to southwestern Australia, or perhaps linked only with antarctic South America.

The stranger to Western Australia must picture the western third of the continent as including divisions which differ very much in climate. The South West is roughly that area south and west of a line from Shark Bay to Esperance: it includes the coastal plain (which lies between the Darling

△ *Banksia ashbyi* E. G. Baker . . .

The *Banksia* family is named after botanist Joseph Banks, who came to Australia with Captain Cook in 1769-1770.

Banksia coccinea R.Br. ▷

Range and the sea), the dairying and fruit-growing districts (in the higher rainfall area) and, inland from these, the wheat belt. The pastoral country lies with one half-circle centred on Carnarvon, and another curving from Broome to Wyndham. Inland from all of these areas are great tracts of sandy, sometimes gravelly, arid country which is very sparsely populated. Sometimes this is undulating and sometimes it consists of sandplains. Beyond this, again, is the "dry heart", largely desert.

To understand why the flora of Western Australia is so largely individual, a glance at a map will show that the State is surrounded on three sides (south, west and north) by ocean, and on the east is bounded by the area of desert. These barriers have proved impassable for most species which might otherwise have invaded the vast area of 2,525,500 square kilometres which is thus confined. In consequence, while much of the general Australian flora has experienced changes due to climatic variations and even oceanic submergence, the South West of Western Australia has remained untouched throughout aeons of time. As a result, many genera have evolved in an unchanged habitat and reached a state of development quite different from plant life in other less tranquil areas. Here the primitive forms have survived in the lovely plants we know today, and with these have developed the more specialised examples which evolution has produced. Nowhere else in the world has such a state of affairs permitted the survival, unchanged and unchanging, of plant life which is almost immeasurably old. It is not, as will be noticed by any traveller, that this survival has been encouraged by genial climatic conditions, good soil and other favourable natural factors. On the contrary: it is frequently in areas of sand and gravel that are to be found the most highly developed types and the most noticeable forms and colours.

Wildflower distribution

This map of Western Australia shows, as far as is practicable, the names of places, localities and rivers referred to in the text, and these give an indication of the distribution of particular wildflowers being discussed.

The regions shown as jarrah and karri forest country indicate only where these trees occur naturally, and it must be understood that large areas within these regions, particularly of jarrah forest, have been cleared and developed as farmlands. This applies also to the jam country.

Lines of rainfall shown are both continuous and broken, for the reason that continuous lines follow boundaries of measured rainfall, whereas broken lines indicate probable limits in areas where rainfall stations are few and far between.

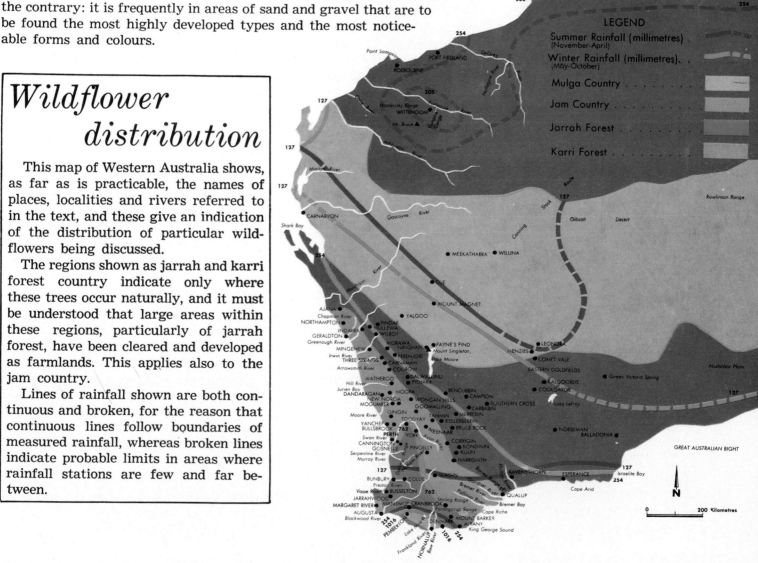

LEGEND

Summer Rainfall (millimetres) (November-April)

Winter Rainfall (millimetres) (May-October)

Mulga Country . . . .

Jam Country . . . .

Jarrah Forest . . . .

Karri Forest . . . .

△ *Grevillea eriostachya* Lindl. . . .
noble plants, flamboyant spikes.

Wildflowers . . .

THE very great diversity and number of native wildflowers of Western Australia often makes their identification—especially by the roadside, in a paddock or when walking in forest country—extremely difficult. Only the acknowledged expert can hope to recognise with certainty most of these, while for the average person, untrained in botany, immediate recognition will sometimes be impossible.

But that does not mean that an intelligent observer is not able to observe "what the flower looks like." He or she will always be able to note where it grows, how it grows, what sort of leaves it has, when it flowers and the type and form of its flowers. And from such careful observation it is often possible for the ordinary wayfarer to say "This, I think, is a hakea" . . . or a crowea or an orchid. Sometimes such an opinion will be wrong, yet by continued interest, by frequently noting the details about many wildflowers, the intelligent man, woman or child can gradually accumulate knowledge as a background to a hobby.

It must be understood that the vast multitude of plants the world over are, for purposes of classification, first divided into main subdivisions. With most of these this book is not concerned for attention is focussed on flowering plants. Of the five main subdivisions the seed bearing plants *(Spermatophytes)* form but one, and this is in turn subdivided again into those in which the seed is enclosed in an ovary *(Angiosperms)* and those with naked seeds *(Gymnosperms),* the cone-bearing plants. It is the *Angiosperms* which include the flowering plants—yet again subdivided into the plants which, when the seed first sprouts, show one seed-leaf *(Monocotyledons)* and those which show two seed-leaves *(Dicotyledons).*

Such groupings of plants are further divided into families, the members of each of which have certain fundamental similarities, thus enabling them to be associated together. The families, in turn, have their own differences —just like branches of a human family!—and for this reason each separate little group within a family is called a genus (a number of which are called genera). Further, still, there are differences within each little group (genus) and the individual members of the genus are called species.

Applying all of this—which, although at first sight may seem involved, on re-reading will become fairly simple—it can be that a lily is a member of the *Liliaceae* (its family), but if it is a fringed lily, it belongs to the genus *Thysanotus,* and it is a particular member of that genus, namely *multiflora* —which specific name describes the plant as many *(multi-)* flowered *(flora).* Again, for example, the Boronias are members of the *Rutaceae,* which family includes the genera *Boronia, Crowea, Diplolaena* and others. But among the members of the genus *Boronia* there are a number of species, of which *Boronia megastigma* is perhaps the best known. Thus that particular species of *Boronia* is differentiated from the remainder by the specific name *mega-*

◁ *Lachnostachys vebascifolia* F.Muell. . . . dense felting to combat a hostile climate.

stigma, meaning great, or large *(mega-) stigma* (referring to that part of the style or ovary-surface which becomes impregnated by pollen). This is perhaps as far as it is necessary to take the general reader, for the wildflowers which will be referred to and illustrated are treated as of general interest to anybody, and therefore botanical science as such is beyond the scope of this book.

It may be as well, nevertheless, to refer to the fact that sometimes names have been changed. For example, *Dryandra sessilis* was formerly called *D. floribunda.* What were called *Mesembryanthemum* are now placed under four distinct genera of *Aizoaceae. Lechenaultia* was until recently spelt *Leschenaultia,* and still retains that spelling in the common name.

It is also as well that comment should be included on the use of common names when writing of some wildflowers. A difficulty arises here for the reason that a name used in the South West relating to a particular flower may be unknown in the wheat belt, where the same flower is called by a different name. More than that, even a third common name may be used along the south coast. For example, when describing *Alyxia buxifolia,* reference is made to the fact that this is sometimes called the camel-bush, and it is also called the dysentery-bush. Equally important, few of the very many Western Australian wildflowers are sufficiently well known to have received a common name. For these reasons, the botanical name of a plant is always to be preferred, for it is accepted and in world-wide use, and is never duplicated.

A word of warning is advisable before consideration is given to the different families of flowering plants dealt with in the following pages. The indiscriminate gathering of wildflowers is at all times to be deprecated. Already some species have entirely disappeared and others are threatened with extinction. The picking of wildflowers is not always essential for identification purposes, for a clear description is most usually all that is necessary for this purpose, but if picking must be resorted to then one stem (of leaf and flower, if possible) is all that is required. In general, wildflowers do not last as cut-flowers (excluding, of course, everlastings and a few others) and the barbaric despoilation of the countryside should not be a characteristic of a civilised people.

Finally, when examining a native plant it should be borne in mind that the colour of the flowers of any given species may vary considerably: soil or seasonal conditions may account for this. The height of a species may also vary from place to place, even from year to year in the same place. Taking all of that into consideration, it is still possible for the visitor to, or the dweller in, any particular area to note from the ensuing chapters on the different families just what wildflowers may be in bloom in a given area at any particular time. If a flower is seen and recognised once or twice it will seldom be forgotten, and gradually a wider knowledge of Western Australian flora will be gained.

PERTH,
Western Australia.

C. A. GARDNER, M.B.E.,
Government Botanist and
Curator of State Herbarium, 1927-61.

△ *Boronia megastigma* Nees . . . so named for its large (mega) stigma.

Caladenia gemmata Lindl. . . . . a beautiful blue china orchid grows in gravel. ▷

LILIACEAE

Lily family

ONE of the largest families of flowering plants, comprising 200 genera and 3,000 species, the Lily family has a wide range over the surface of the earth. It may be surprising to some readers to know that the magnificent lilies in gardens all over the world are of the same family as the blackboys *(Xanthorrhoea)* of Western Australia, or that the lordly tulips and exquisite hyacinths so admired by flower lovers everywhere are similarly related to wax-flowers *(Burchardia)* which thrive in the sandy woodlands of our coastal plain, yet this is so.

Western Australia is rich in plants of this family, with 101 species and 31 genera. These include *Xanthorrhoea* and *Burchardia,* already mentioned, the fringed lilies *(Thysanotus),* the blind grasses *(Stypandra),* the false blind grasses *(Agrostocrinum), Sowerbaea,* pin-grass

△ A blackboy *Xanthorrhoea preissii* Endl. at Augusta which is 5.5 metres tall and probably 200 years old.

△ These milkmaids *Burchardia umbellata* R.Br. belong to the same botanical family as the blackboy.

(Borya), the rush lilies *(Johnsonia),* the tinsel lily or Star of Bethlehem *(Calectasia),* and *Kingia,* commonly called the grass-tree.

By far the greater number of these are native to the woodlands of the South West, and, in the spring months between September and December, to come upon a more open patch of ground dotted with lovely little clumps of the fringed lily *(Thysanotus multiflorus)* or groupings of *Burchardia multiflora* is to appreciate the appeal which these most attractive little flowers can exert. *T. sparteus* is rush-like, with a large underground tuber, but is leafless at the time of flowering. Another species of *Burchardia (B. umbellata)* is found in moist, sandy soils: these have rather broad leaves, especially at the base, short thick flower stems and purple anthers.

Found in association with granite rocks are the two blind-grasses indigenous to Western Australia. *Stypandra imbricata* is common along the south coast as far east as Esperance and north to Geraldton. Its bright blue flowers among the granite

10

Lily family

Th. Patternii 8/31

△ False blind-grass *Agrostocrinum scabrum* (R.Br.) Baill. is also known as the bluegrass lily.

△ Fringed lily *Thysanotus multiflorus* R.Br.

△ Blue squill *Chamaescilla corymbosa* (R.Br.) F.Muell.

▽ Black gins or grass-trees *Kingia australis* R.Br. near the mouth of the Waychinicup River.

▽ *Stypandra imbricata* R.Br. is poisonous

△ Vanilla lily *Sowerbaea laxiflora* Lindl.

△ Blue tinsel-lily *Calectasia cyanea* R.Br.
▽ Dwarf burchardia *Burchardia multiflora* Lindl.

outcrops are a most attractive sight, but this plant is poisonous to sheep and horses. Another species *(S. grandiflora)* with broader, paler leaves is found in the jarrah and karri forests.

False blind-grass *(Agrostocrinum scabrum)*, also called the bluegrass-lily, is at once conspicuous and handsome because of the rich colouring of its beautifully formed petals, which later become twisted after flowering. This plant occurs in various types of soil from the vicinity of Gingin south to the coast and as far east as Esperance.

Other species of the lily family in Western Australia which although not illustrated must not be overlooked are the lovely species of *Caesia* and *Chamaescilla* which are to be found growing in shady spots almost anywhere near Perth, and the rush-lily *(Johnsonia lupulina)*, with drooping spikes of flowers hidden beneath pink or white overlapping scales, that is to be found near Albany.

Another and a peculiarly pleasing member of this family is the delicate *Sowerbaea laxiflora*, with umbels of pale purple flowers and grass-like leaves, while the blue tinsel-lily *(Calectasia cyanea)* is frequently to be seen growing in the sandy soil around Perth during the days of early spring.

The blackboy *(Xanthorrhoea)* is one of the most peculiar members of the lily family. A blackboy may grow to a height of 5.5 metres, averaging perhaps 25 mm in vertical growth each year. It represents an ancient type of plant.

▽ *Dasypogon hookeri* Drumm. grows in damp places in the heavy rainfall forest areas of the South West.

HAEMODORACEAE

Kangaroo-paw family

A NUMBER of the genera of this relatively small family are restricted in distribution to the South West. The family name is taken from the genus *Haemodorum,* the bloodroots—plants usually (in the South West entirely) with black flowers and richly coloured red subterranean parts formerly used medicinally by the Aborigines.

Apart from *Haemodorum* and the hairless white-flowered genus *Phlebocarya*—the latter with two species found in poor sandy soils—members of this family are characterised locally by unusually-coloured flowers densely covered with woolly hairs.

It is this combination of factors which led to the choice of the species *Anigozanthos manglesii* as the State's floral emblem.

Indeed, the bizarre effect of two sharply contrasting colours of this and a few other species renders the kangaroo-paws singularly arresting and attractive.

The principal genera are *Anigozanthos,* with tubular, irregular-shaped flowers and fruits containing numerous small seeds; *Macropidia,* the true kangaroo-paw, named from the Greek word for "long-footed" and having three seeds to each flower; *Blancoa,* the red bugle; *Conostylis,* with very hairy yellow (rarely white) cone-flowers; and *Tribonanthes,* small tuberous-rooted plants of moist situations with white flowers of felt-like texture.

In the first the flowers are borne in single spikes at the top of the flowering stem. The most common is the dwarf catspaw (*A. humilis*) which inhabits the sandy country of the west-

△ *Anigozanthos manglesii* D.Don, best known of the kangaroo-paws, grows profusely in Kings Park.

ern coastal plain, extending inland as far as Kellerberrin and Kulin, and southwards to the Albany district. The flowers are yellow suffused with red, sometimes more red than yellow, and the plant rarely exceeds 300 mm in height. It always occurs in sand. A yellow-flowered form is also known.

A second species, and the one which is perhaps best known because it is fairly common in cultivation, is the Mangle's kangaroo-paw (*A. manglesii*) which occurs in sandy soil, its area of natural distribution extending from the Murchison River in the north to Busselton and Lake Muir in the south. This species has long flowering stems of a deep red or purple, and large individual flowers which are of a metallic green with the exception of the red ovary at the base.

Anigozanthos bicolor has much the appearance of *A. manglesii,* being similarly red and green in colour, i.e. the flowers are green and the stalks red, but the green is of a lighter hue, being sometimes almost yellow, and the flower is contracted

◁ Black kangaroo-paw *Macropidia fuliginosa* (Hook.) Druce.

13

Budginga
9/3

△ Red bugle *Blancoa canescens* Lindl.

▽ Dwarf cats-paw *Anigozanthos humilis* Lindl.

△ The green kangaroo-paw *Anigozanthos viridis* Endl.

▽ White coneflower *Conostylis setosa* Lindl.

△ The kangaroo-paw *Anigozanthos manglesii* D.Don. is the floral emblem of Western Australia. It thrives in sandy soil from the Murchison River in the north, south to the Busselton area.

in number, but what they lack numerically is more than compensated by size and richness of colour. The plant has a limited area of distribution around King George Sound where it grows in peaty soil, usually in protected situations in the woodland.

Anigozanthos flavidus is not well named. The colour of ·the flowers varies from pale green to yellow, or sometimes red. It is the largest of all the kangaroo-paws, often exceeding three metres in stature, with long broad grass-like leaves often two metres long. It occurs in the swampy areas of the karri forest, around Albany and northwards to Busselton, but is hardy in cultivation in almost any soil.

The two remaining species are perhaps the most popular: *Anigozanthos pulcherrimus* has large panicles of woolly flowers of a rich golden yellow, sometimes suffused with red, especially on the stems and lower portion of the flowers. It flowers in mid-December, and is fairly common on the sandplain country northwards from the Moore River as far as the Arrowsmith River. It grows freely in the poorest sand, and examples may be found as far south as the Gingin Brook. Under good conditions it attains a height of about two metres, but is usually smaller. Its flowering

△ *Anigozanthos flavidus* D.C. . . . biggest of the kangaroo-paws.

upwards, whereas in *A. manglesii* the apex is expanded. *A. bicolor* grows in places which are wet in winter, and it rarely exceeds 450 mm in height. Common around King George Sound it extends northwards as far as the Moore River, being common in depressions and on the marshy banks of watercourses.

Anigozanthos viridis is the green kangaroo-paw. This species has flowers of metallic green, and the same colour characterises the stems. It extends from the Moore River southwards to the Busselton district, and is invariably found in low-lying places, wet in winter, where the subsoil consists of clay.

The remaining species in the second group are characterised by having forked or branched flowering stems. *Anigozanthos preissii* has the stems once-forked at the top, and the individual flowers are the largest of the genus. They are a rich orange colour suffused with red, and are at least 50 mm in length, curved downwards, with narrower and deeper divisions than the other species. The flowers rarely exceed seven

Anigozanthos pulcherrimus Hook. . . . . grows freely in the ▷
poorest sand.

△ *Patersonia occidentalis* R.Br. and △ *Patersonia xanthina* F. Muell. . . . two varieties of the native iris.

IRIDACEAE

Iris family

season coincides with two other orange-yellow plants—the Christmas tree *Nuytsia floribunda* and the orange *Verticordia nitens,* and sometimes the three may be seen growing together.

The last species of true kangaroo-paws is *Anigozanthos rufus,* the first species to receive a name. It is common between Esperance and Ravensthorpe, but extends in less abundance to the Stirling Range, and occurs in sand. It has all the characteristics of *A. pulcherrimus,* but the flowers are a deep burgundy purple, and the leaves are not hairy—the latter character being restricted to *A. pulcherrimus.*

The black kangaroo-paw (*Macropidia fuliginosa*) is generally limited to the sandplains northwards from Perth almost to Geraldton, but sometimes occurs in ironstone gravelly soils. It has differently shaped and more deeply divided flowers than *Anigozanthos.*

Common in the Hill River district yet occurring sporadically as far south as Gosnells, the handsome red bugle (*Blancoa canescens*) flowers in winter and early spring.

Of *Conostylis* there are nearly 40 species, the flowers of all of which are usually yellow, rarely white, and symmetrical. These are clothed with densely branched hairs. The flowers are regular like those of *Blancoa* but there are differences in details of the seed attachment. *Conostylis setosa* is common in the gravelly soils of the Darling Range near Perth. It attains a stature of about 400 mm and flowers in September and October.

The family *Haemodoraceae* differs from the *Liliaceae* only in the position of the ovary, which is placed below the insertion of the perianth or petals.

Orthrosanthus multiflorus Sweet . . . eight species, five in Western Australia, three in the Andes. ▷

THIS is a family which, including such weeds as the Cape tulip, Guildford grass and the like (mainly of African origin), also numbers among its members many very attractive garden plants, e.g. crocus, iris, freesia, gladiolus and crocosmia, and two genera of wildflowers indigenous to Western Australia. These are the native iris (*Patersonia*) and the morning iris (*Orthrosanthus*).

The fourteen local species of native iris all grow in the southern part of this State. *Patersonia* has only three petal-like perianth-segments and the flowers are violet in colour with the single exception of the yellow-flowered *P. xanthina* which loves the shady recesses of the jarrah and karri forests. *P. occidentalis* and *P. umbrosa* much resemble each other and both grow freely in sandy places. Some of the smaller forms extend eastwards to the Southern Cross area, but most are to be found in regions of higher rainfall, and flowering in the period August-November, although *P. occidentalis,* common around Perth, continues in blossom until the summer. The flowers are all very delicate in texture and wither early in the day.

17

Similarly with morning iris; a touch of real heat and the flowers wither by afternoon. There are but eight species of *Orthrosanthus* found in the world and five of these are native to the wetter parts of our South West. (The other three species are found in southern South America in the region of the Andes.) The five species in question resemble one another, apart from the number of flowers on a stem which may vary from few to many, but they are alike in preferring humus soils and shady places.

Plants of this family can usually be distinguished by the presence of only three stamens which are placed opposite to the outer of the six (rarely three) petals, and the position of the ovary—which, as with the Amaryllis family, is situated below the petals.

ORCHIDACEAE

Orchid family

OF ALMOST infinite variety in habit of growth and floral structure, the Orchid family has a great attraction for both botanist and horticulturist, mainly because of the especially handsome appearance of the flowers of many species.

All are perennial plants: they occur as epiphytes on the trunks and branches of trees; as terrestrial plants with tubers in the soil, or as saprophytes which, devoid of leaves, are dependent on other organic matter for their existence.

The family is a large one, including as it does some 450 genera and a total of about 15,000 species of wide distribution. They are abundant in the tropics, where the greater number occur as tree orchids. On the other hand, most of the orchids of the temperate and cooler regions are plants growing in the soil: such die down to the ground annually but have tubers which persist until the following growing season.

Twenty-five genera and numerous species of orchids are found in Western Australia. Three of these are found in the Kimberley Division, two of which grow on the trunks and branches of trees. In the South West all of the known varieties grow in the soil—but the remarkable *Rhizanthella gardneri,* the subterranean orchid, which has a lily-like inflorescence with crowded, dark coloured flowers in the base of its tube, is found below the surface of the soil. It has not been seen growing undisturbed, for it was first discovered at Corrigin during ploughing operations, when the plants were upturned.

Many of the orchids in Western Australia are now "protected plants." Some were formerly abundant in the metropolitan area but are becoming scarce.

A variety of soils and situations seem to have favoured different species. The red-beak orchid (*Lyperanthus nigricans*) favours a shady spot in the South West, flowers only after a bushfire.

The unsurpassed blue-lady orchid (*Thelymitra crinita*), which grows to a height of one metre and will bear seven to seventeen sky-blue

◁ Red-beak orchid *Lyperanthus nigricans* R.Br.

△ Blue-lady orchid *Thelymitra crinita* Lindl.

△ Vanilla orchid *Thelymitra antennifera* (Lindl.) Hook.

△ Bird orchid *Pterostylis barbata* Lindl.

△ Purple enamelled orchid *Elythranthera brunonis* (Endl.) A. S. George.

ORCHID FAMILY

Red Spider orchid
8/30
N of Winterm

flowers, occurs freely in the clay soils of the Darling Range and also in humid, sandy patches on the coastal plain from slightly north of Perth southwards round to King George Sound. The leopard orchid *(T. fusco-lutea)* grows at the foot of the Darling Range and the vanilla orchid *(T. antennifera)*occurs in moist soils near granite rocks.

Found in shady spots of the jarrah forest, the bird orchid with its green hood *(Pterostylis barbata)* is distributed over a wide area in the lower South West but it is never abundant.

The white spider-orchid *(Caladenia patersonii)* can be found in the woodlands of the South West as far north as Geraldton, while the cowslip orchid *(C. flava)* is found in similar coastal situations yet also as far inland as Mullewa, Bencubbin and Merredin. The dwarf blue orchid *(C. sericea)* with the charm and delicacy of a wood-violet, can be discovered in various parts of the South West, and the enamelled orchid *(Elythranthera emarginata)* also likes sandy soil in the south-west corner, as far north as the Greenough River.

Tower orchid
8/29

△ White spider orchid *Caladenia patersonii* R.Br.var.longicauda (Lindl.) R. S. Rogers.

△ Cowslip orchid *Caladenia flava* R.Br.

Tall leek orchid *Prasophyllum elatum* R.Br. ▷

Shell or jug greenhood *Pterostylis recurva* Benth. ▷ ▷

Darling
Range 9/5

△ King spider orchid *Caladenia huegelii* Reichb. f.

△ Bee orchid *Caladenia discoidea* Lindl.

△ Pink enamelled orchid *Elythranthera emarginata* (Lindl.)
A. S. George.

△ Pink fairies orchid *Caladenia latifolia* R.Br.

△ *Petrophile divaricata* R.Br. grows high up in the Stirling Range.

PROTEACEAE

Banksia family

SHOWING an extraordinary diversity of forms of foliage—often in the same species—this family well warrants the name *Proteaceae,* derived from Proteus, the mythical son of Poseidon, who could change his form at will.

The family is widely dispersed over the temperate parts of the southern hemisphere, but it is particularly richly developed in South Africa and Australia, extending northwards into the mountains of Abyssinia and into the tropics of Australia. There are 55 genera and about 1200 species; of these 475 occur in Africa and about 700 in Australia. In Western Australia 480 species are to be found and the greater number of these are confined to the South West.

The flowers of the many related plants differ considerably in appearance and it is therefore as well for the general reader to realise that only a few of the better-known species of *Isopogon,* of *Petrophile,* or *Grevillea* or other genera are here illustrated or described.

The round-headed drumstick *(Isopogon sphaerocephalus)* is a common shrub of the gravelly soils of the Darling Range, extending southwards to Jarrahwood. It rarely exceeds a metre in height, has straight upright stems, and flowers from September to November. *I. latifolius,* in contrast, attains a height of 2.5 to 3 metres and is the largest flowered species of the genus. It resembles a rhododendron when in bloom. Inhabiting the high hills of the Stirling Range, it is usually found in elevated situations among rocks, and flowers in October. *I. formosus* is a handsome and attractive shrub of the same district but, found in stony places, it rarely exceeds a metre in height. It flowers at the same time as *I. latifolius.* Smaller still is *I. dubius* which infrequently exceeds 450 mm in height. This last has harsh, prickly foliage but attractive heads of rose-pink flowers that are a common sight in August and September in the clay soils of the Darling Range.

◁ The round-headed drumstick, *Isopogon sphaerocephalus* Lindl., is a common shrub in the Darling Range.

Isopogon latifolius R.Br. grows in the high hills of the Stirling Range. ▷

The flowers of *Isopogon*—and of *Petrophile*—are arranged in cones and, as the flowers fade, the scales at the bases of the individual flowers become enlarged. These scales fall off in the case of *Isopogon* but with *Petrophile* the scales of the cones remain persistent even after the nuts (seeds) have fallen.

Of *Petrophile* there are 30 species in south-western Australia. *P. biloba* is a shrub of from 1.25 to 2.5 metres in height which occurs in the clay soils of the Darling Range with leafy spikes of pink flowers.

Seemingly quite different—yet closely related—are the species of *Adenanthos* which can usually be recognised by their scarlet flowers and long styles. These flowers are solitary—not in clusters or spikes. It is to be noted that the long style of the flower remains curved before the perianth opens—as with *Grevillea*, *Hakea* and *Banksia*. There are 17 species of *Adenanthos*, and of these *A. barbigera* is a small shrub, common between Toodyay and Busselton, usually found in gravelly soil. A larger flowered species, *A. obovata*, is found in swampy places.

Turning now to *Conospermum*, these are widely known as smoke-bushes because of their typically grey flowers which may be woolly in appearance. These usually overtop the foliage and, seen from a distance in masses, resemble smoke. Yet this is not true of all species for with some the flower is quite different; such may be devoid of wool or hairs and be white, blue or pink in colour. Australia as a whole can boast 40 species, of which 27 are found in the South West or in the Eastern Goldfields. The commonest of Western Australian species is *C. stoechadis* of the sand-plains of the interior. *C. triplinervium* is the largest of this genus and is a shrub of the metropolitan area with three-veined leaves. *C. amoenum* is a blue-flowered species found in the Stirling Range, and *C. crassinervium* has a range extending from Jurien Bay to Bullsbrook. This latter species, with but few leaves arising from the soil, has tall slender stems which carry at their ends the remarkable grey plumes of the inflorescence.

One of the most outstanding members of the family *Proteaceae* is undoubtedly the genus

△ *Isopogon formosus* R.Br. . . . a handsome shrub in the Stirlings.
▽ *Isopogon dubius* (R.Br.) Druce . . . common in the Darling Range.

▽ *Petrophile biloba* R.Br. likes the clay soil of the Darling Range.

△ *Adenanthos barbigera* Lindl. . . . scarlet flowers, long styles.

△ *Grevillea wilsonii* A. Cunn., a small shrub of the jarrah forest.

named *Grevillea*. Its species number 175, and, with the exception of a few in New Caledonia, these are confined to Australia—and most of them to this State. Of the Western Australian species the greater number are in the south, but some extend to the Kimberley division and those are mostly trees.

Few plants are more attractive, for the flowers of characteristic shape range through the colours of fire—intense scarlet, crimson, orange, yellow and white. These shrubs are most easily recognisable by the shell-like fruit which falls in the same season in which the flowers appear, and the most attractive plants are those on which the flowers are in one-sided "spikes." In some they are in small clusters.

Grevillea wilsonii is a small shrub of the jarrah forest occurring in gravelly soils and flowering from September until December. It rarely exceeds 1.25 metres in height and is of a dense, bushy habit, with finely divided pungent-pointed leaves. In contrast, the flamboyant, deep orange spikes of *G. excelsior* that crown this noble plant, which often attains a height of six metres, are a feature of the yellow sandy areas of the southern interior. *G. excelsior* looks rather like a pine tree and flowers in late October and November. Less attractive south-western species are *G. pilulifera* of the Darling Range and *G. synaphéae* both of which flower in the spring.

△ The most common of the West Australian smoke-bushes, *Conospermum stoechadis* Endl.

Represented in even the arid heart of Australia —where, as in the north of Western Australia, the indigenous species are commonly known as "beefwoods" and the stems are used for fence posts— the species of *Hakea* number over 100, but of these 86 are found in this State. Some of the southern species are of horticultural value and among these are *H. laurina,* the "pin-cushion," commonly found in gardens, the remarkable *H. victoriae,* which comes from the Bremer River and has large variegated leaves of many colours, and several others.

Hakea petiolaris is not common, but it can be found among granite rocks between Mundaring and York. The somewhat striking *H. bucculenta,* with spikes of orange or intense scarlet flowers, has its home between Indarra and Pindar, being a shrub of 4.5 metres in height, with narrow, bright green leaves occurring in the thickets, while the closely related *H. multilineata* is common throughout the interior.

The native pears belong to the genus *Xylomelum* and there are three species, one in eastern Australia and two in south-western Australia. The common species of the jarrah forest, *X occidentale,* has broad holly-like leaves and rusty-brown fruits. The sandplain pear, *X angustifolium,* on the other hand, has narrow, entire leaves and silver-grey fruits. Both species flower in December and January, the latter with its masses of creamy white blossoms being a feature of the sandplains at that time of the year.

△ *Hakea bucculenta* C. A. Gardn., orange, scarlet spikes.
▽ *Hakea cucullata* R.Br. . . . hood-leaved hakea.

▽ The sandplain pear, *Xylomelum angustifolium* Kipp.. carries masses of creamy white blossoms in December and January.

△ *Hakea victoriae* Drumm. is a unique species which occurs on the south coast near the Barren Range.

△ The pin-cushion Hakea, *Hakea laurina R.Br.*

A closer look at *Hakea victoriae.* ▷

△ *Banksia coccinea* R.Br. . . . Scarlet Banksia of the south.

△ *Banksia baxteri* R.Br. at Lookout Point near Cheyne Beach, on the south coast.

The species of the magnificent genus *Banksia* are perhaps the most attractive of all the plants of the bush, for when in bloom they carry amazingly fine spikes or cones of densely packed, spirally arranged flowers. This genus comprises 51 species, all confined to Australia, and of these 41 are native to Western Australia and only one of these latter is found outside this State. Many of these are in cultivation in other lands and much prized as horticultural plants. Among the most attractive are the scarlet *B. coccinea* of the south coast, the crimson *B. occidentalis* of the same area. *B. quercifolia* has oak-like leaves and deep orange spikes of flowers. Others are orange, yellow, purple or green. Swamp Banksia (*B. littoralis*) is a common tree from the Moore River down to the south coast in areas which are swampy, at least during the winter months. It attains a height of 9 metres and has a somewhat distinctive habit of growth, in that the branches are often widely spread or drooping. It flowers from April till August. With few exceptions, all of the species are inhabitants of sandy soil, whether of the woodland, the forest or the open plain. The holly-leaved Banksia (*B. ilicifolia*) is the only species which does not produce spikes of flowers.

△ *Banksia laricina* C. A. Gardn.

△ *Banksia media* R.Br.

△ *Banksia menziesii* R.Br.

△ *Banksia lindleyana* Meisn.

△ *Banksia occidentalis* R. Br.

△ *Banksia caleyi* R.Br.

△ Oak-leaved Banksia
Banksia quercifolia R.Br.

△ Woolly-spiked Banksla
Banksia baueri R.Br.

△ *Banksia burdettii* Bak. f.

△ ▽ *Dryandra praemorsa* Meisn. . . . cut-leaf Dryandra.

▽ *Dryandra sessilis* (Knight) Domin. . . . parrot bush.

△ *Dryandra formosa* R.Br. is one of the most spectacular wildflowers of the Stirling Range.

Last to receive attention is the genus *Dryandra,* which is common in south-western Australia. There are 48 species, most of which are low shrubs of varied appearance. A few are tall, exceeding three metres in height but mostly they are less than 600 mm high. Some of the species are of limited occurrence and are in danger of extinction, examples being the resplendent *D. speciosa* and the notable *D. vestita,* both formerly common on the Tammin sand heath. The species depicted *(D. sessilis)* is the common parrot bush of the limestone coastal area, but this extends as far inland as Southern Cross, being found in association with granite rocks. (It was formerly known as *D. floribunda).*

△ *Banksia victoriae* Meisn. The magnificent Banksias are perhaps the most attractive of all the plants of the bush. They are found only in Australia and 41 species are native to Western Australia.

SANTALACEAE

Sandalwood family

DERIVING some of their nourishment from the roots of other plants by means of sucker-like attachments on the roots of the host-plant, the members of the Sandalwood family are all parasites. They are related to the Mistletoe family (also parastic plants) but differ from the latter in the absence of any external cup to the flower, and whereas the mistletoes (excepting only *Nuytsia floribunda*) occur as parasites on the branches of trees, plants of the Sandalwood family occur as shrubs or trees, with roots in the soil. The sandalwoods have a wide range in the Goldfields and mulga country, while in the South West they are almost entirely limited to jam country.

Best known of the *Santalaceae* are the two sandalwoods and the quandong, or native peach. The sandalwoods are of value because of the oil of the stems and roots: one, *Santalum lanceolatum,* is found in the region of summer rains, and has small dark purple fruits, while the other, *S. spicatum,* is the common sandalwood of the southern areas of Western Australia and has larger fruits, which are green or brown when ripe.

The quandong *(S. acuminatum)* is a well known and attractive tree over a wide area of country. Its greenish white flowers are succeeded by fruits which are bright red. These are edible, sometimes being made into preserves, but

△ The quandong, *Santalum acuminatum* (R.Br.) D.C., grows over a wide area of Western Australia

the edible part is small, the greater part of the fruit consisting of the stone. Such are a favourite article of food of the emu, and there is little doubt that this bird does much to spread the seed.

The remaining members of the Sandalwood family are not particularly attractive, being—with two or three exceptions—small shrubs with much reduced leaves and minute flowers. Of the larger species of these one of the more attractive is *Exocarpos sparteus,* a small tree with numerous graceful branches; these bear ultimate branches which often hang vertically. *Exocarpos* is the native cherry, or "the fruit with the stone outside," the true fruit being borne at the end of a berry-like receptacle, or stalk, thus giving the impression that the apparent fruit has an external seed.

The floral features of plants of *Santalaceae* are much like those of *Proteaceae,* except that the ovary is joined to the perianth (petal-like portion) or to a disc which surrounds or lies upon its summit.

◁ The fruit of the quandong is a favourite food of the emu, which has done much to spread the seed.

△ *Nuytsia floribunda* (Labill.) R.Br., the Christmas tree . . . one of the most remarkable of trees.

LORANTHACEAE

Mistletoe family

THE plants of this family are mainly shrubs which are hemiparasitic (half parasites) on the branches of trees, and the fruit is a sticky or viscid berry.

Closely related to the true mistletoe of Europe (*Viscum album*) are the many species of mistletoe which grow on the branches of a number of Western Australian trees and are also distributed over the warmer regions of the globe. These mostly have bright scarlet or red flowers and red or pink berries.

Exceptional in this family is the Christmas tree (*Nuytsia floribunda*) of south-western Australia. Trees with greater abundance of flowers are rare. Add to this the warmth and brilliance of the flowers, which are of a pure cadmium orange, projected against our summer blue skies, and we have one of the finest and most remarkable trees.

AMARANTHACEAE

Amaranth family

△ Christmas tree blooms . . . warmth and brilliance.

This exceptional tree perpetuates the name of Peter Nuyts who was chief passenger on the "Gulden Zeepard" which visited these shores in the year 1627. An exhaustive examination was made of the coastline lying to the north of the Great Australian Bight which became known for some 150 years as Nuytsland.

N. floribunda is remarkable because it is a parasite yet it is an independent tree growing in the ground and receiving only some of its food from the roots of nearby host-trees and with a different habit of growth from the common mistletoes. It is further remarkable because unlike its relatives—and, in fact, most common plants—its seeds produce not two but from three to six seed-leaves, or cotyledons.

The trunks attain a great size, especially in girth, but the wood is very soft and fibrous, and thus the tree is unsafe for climbing, even by small children. It is native only to this State and its range extends from the Murchison River in the north to the south coast as far east as Israelite Bay, and as far inland as Harrismith and Yorkrakine Hill, near Kellerberrin. It is always found in sand or associated with granite rocks. It flowers most freely when the country in which it grows has been burned by bush fires.

The family can usually be distinguished by the inferior ovary, the perianth, coloured and petal-like, its segments free or united with the stamens of the same number and opposite to them, and the presence of a small cup which is external to the flower and forms, as it were, a cup below the petals or perianth segments.

P LENTIFUL in the tropical and sub-tropical regions of the globe—especially in America, Africa, and Australia—the Amaranth family comprises 64 genera and about 800 species, yet it is not a family rich in garden subjects if we except the well known amaranthus, the bachelor's button (*Gomphrena*), the cockscomb (*Celosia*) and a few others.

The plants of this family indigenous to Western Australia are represented mainly by the numerous species of *Ptilotus* and *Gomphrena*. The last named is confined to the tropical north but the others are more generally distributed, although most abundant in the dry soils of the interior where they become a feature of the landscape after the spring and autumn rains.

△ Weeping mulla-mulla, *Ptilotus calostachyus* (F.Muell.) F.Muell. growing in Yampire Gorge, near Wittenoom.

△ Tall mulla-mulla, *Ptilotus exaltatus* Nees. in mulga country between Roebourne and Wittenoom.

In this respect the species of most interest is *P. rotundifolius* which is found in clay or stony soils between the Hamersley Range and Meekatharra. This is a shrub, sometimes a metre tall, with large flannel-like leaves and large spikes of rose-pink flowers which are produced in such abundance that, when in blossom, the plants can be seen from a considerable distance.

In the mulga country are to be found a number of plants which are attractive in the same way—spikes of densely crowded blossoms, purple in *P. helipteroides* and the tall *P. exaltatus,* the leaves of the latter being broad and green (and these can be used to provide an excellent salad!). There are to be seen, also, the massive green spikes of *P. macrocephalus* or the delicate *P. calostachyus* of the Roebourne and Port Hedland areas, a species with long, wiry stems carrying slender rose-pink spikes of flowers with pointed tips.

△ The broad green leaves of *Ptilotus exaltatus* make an excellent salad!

AIZOACEAE

Pigface family

△ *Gomphrena flaccida* R.Br. . . . grows in the better soils on river banks and depressions in the tropical north.

Although in the South West there are many fewer species, a number of these are attractive— *P. manglesii* which is summer flowering on the coastal plain and in parts of the Darling Range, and the green-spiked mulla-mulla *(P. poly-stachyus)* which is eaten by stock.

Ptilotus is common in the north of Western Australia, but a well-known species of the South West is the small pussy-tailed *P. humilis* which is a feature of the agricultural areas in late spring. It has prostrate stems and densely silky spikes of green flowers suffused with yellow.

The other of our indigenous genera, *Gomphrena,* differs from *Ptilotus* in having its leaves opposite to one another. It is a characteristic genus of the Kimberley district, where *G. canescens* occurs in drifts, noteworthy because of the handsome clover-like heads of numerous rose-pink blossoms. This is a favourite food of horses and cattle.

While flowering seasons with species of *Gomphrena* and *Ptilotus* in the north occur during the summer months, and in the South West the usual flowering season for *Ptilotus* is during late spring, in the mulga country, on the other hand, flowering occurs at any time after rain—which means that for some plants found there the season may be short or extended to cover both summer and winter months.

Rose-tipped mulla-mulla *Ptilotus manglesii* (Lindl.) F.Muell. ▷

◁ On the track through the Hamersley Ranges to Mt. Bruce *Ptilotus helipteroides* (F.Muell.) F.Muell., hairy mulla-mulla.

EMBODYING more than 600 species arranged under about 100 genera, the pigface family is not a large one and is indigenous mainly to South Africa. A number of plants of South African origin are commonly grown in gardens in Western Australia; they are densely tufted or trailing plants with flowers of brilliant colours and do much to brighten the summer aspect of gardens in the Perth district. In all there are 13 genera and 30 species native to this State. All are classed as succulents: they have fleshy leaves or, in the case of a few, are leafless.

Among the leafless forms—or, more exactly, forms which possess small scales instead of leaves —is the genus *Macarthuria* with two species, one of which *M. australis* is common in the sandy soils of the western littoral from the Murchison River southwards to Albany. This forms wiry, untidy growths, flowers late into summer and is very common around Perth.

△ The common ice-plant, *Gasoul crystallinum* (L.) Roth.

The common pigface plant *(Carpobrotus edulis)* is colloquially known elsewhere as the Hottentot fig, and there is another equally wide-spread seaside species, *C. aequilaterus,* and both of these extend from the Murchison River to the Bunbury district. Other plants which might be classed as "pigface" are *Mesembryanthemum floribundum* and *Disphyma blackii.* The latter is not common and is found mainly on the shores of the inland salt-pans. Other types are the ice-plants— species of *Cryophytum,* one of which is a common weed in certain sandy inland areas. Then there is the New Zealand spinach *(Tetragonia tetragonoides),* common in some sandy coastal areas and cultivated sometimes as an edible spinach, and five other species of this genus *(Tetragonia),* three of which favour coastal situations and two the salt areas of the interior.

Of this family's northern representatives there are a number of tropical genera, the species of which do not extend farther south than the Minilya River. These include the species of *Trianthema,* one of which *(T. pilosa),* is common in the Kimberley, and extends its long prostrate

△ *Carpobrotus edulis* (L.)N.E. Br. . . . the common pigface, also known as the Hottentot fig.

stems over the red sand. Its young leaves are a deep violet, and these contrast beautifully with the pink flowers.

More curious are the species of *Aizoon* (from which the family takes its name) found on the flats and in the lake country of the eastern Murchison and Goldfields. These plants have four petal-like calyx-lobes which are brightly coloured inside, white, yellow or green, and have thick, fleshy leaves.

Normally *Aizoaceae* occur in two environments: the sand close to the sea or to the larger inland saltpans, or the saline clay soils of the interior. Both, however, have this in common—they are physiologically dry, and this accounts mainly for the succulent, water-storing tissues.

In general the flowers of this family do not possess petals, these being replaced by infertile flattened staminal filaments which resemble petals: such are often numerous, as in the case of the pigface plants. (It should be noted that what were formerly known as *Mesembryanthemum* are now placed under four distinct genera of *Aizoaceae;* many have midday flowers, opening only under conditions of bright sunlight).

◁ *Trianthema pilosa* F.Muell.

Disphyma blackii Chinnock, formerly known as *Disphyma* ▷ *australe,* grows on the shores of inland salt-pans.

RANUNCULACEAE

Buttercup family

THE family to which the buttercup *(Ranunculus)* belongs is an extensive one, numbering some 35 genera with 1,500 species. Its members are found in the cool temperate regions of the earth, particularly in the northern hemisphere, and include a number of garden plants of such widely differentiated genera as *Ranunculus, Anemone, Delphinium,* larkspur, columbine *(Aquilegia),* love-in-the-mist *(Nigella)* and peony *(Paeonia)*—all of which are herbaceous—and the climbing species of *Clematis.*

Few families exhibit such variation and it is not possible in a book such as this to give the reader any idea of what exactly constitutes the status of the family. It is, however, very closely related to the *Hibbertia* family, from which it differs essentially in that the plants of *Ranunculaceae* are herbs (without woody or persistent stems) or climbers, never shrubs (as in *Hibbertia*) and the sepals are deciduous.

The Western Australian members of the family are, with two exceptions, all found in the South West. There are two species of *Clematis* with white flowers and three yellow-flowered buttercups *(Ranunculus),* while in the dry interior there is to be found a curious dwarfed annual *(Myosurus minimus)* with narrow, grass-like leaves and small yellow flowers bearing in the centre a spike of carpels.

△ *Clematis pubescens* Hueg. is a common climber which grows 2.5 to 3 metres high.

Of the two species of *Clematis*—the name is derived from the Greek *klema,* a vine or shoot— *C. pubescens* is a pure white flowered climber common in the Geraldton district, in the coastal areas and the jarrah forest, and conspicuous during its flowering season in September and October. It attains a height of 2.5 to 3 metres, climbing over rocks and shrubs, and the flower has not petals but four (rarely five) sepals which are petal-like in their appearance and consistence. The stamens are numerous and the many fruiting carpels each terminate in a long plumed tail. A second species, *C. microphylla,* is rare, and found only inland; it sometimes has unisexual flowers and narrow leaves.

The common buttercup *(Ranunculus colonorum)* is a perennial herb found only in shady woods and is not uncommon in the tuart forest, in the region of the lower Blackwood River and near Perth. Its round leaves are deeply cut into lobes and it bears rich yellow flowers on long stalks.

DROSERACEAE

Forrer Cluttering 8/29

Sundew family

THE ABILITY to trap and digest insects to augment their nitrogen supply is a common characteristic of plants of the *Drosera* family, and to this end curious mechanisms are employed.

The most extraordinary is that of the plant known as Venus' fly-trap *(Dionaea muscipula)* which is a botanical oddity. It has leaves with a broad leaf-like leaf-stalk, surmounted by a two-lobed leaf-blade with long hairs on the margins and sensitive hairs on the leaf-blade surface. These two lobes close upwards when the leaf is touched, the marginal hairs interlock making a perfect trap, and the imprisoned victim is digested by means of secretions from glands on the inner surface of the leaf.

The sundews *(Drosera)* have a general distribution which embraces the tropical and temperate regions of the globe, although they are best represented in the southern mountains (Andean) parts of South America and in south-western Australia.

△ *Drosera menziesii* R.Br.

△ *Drosera gigantea* Lindl. . . . giant sundew.

△ *Drosera macrantha* Endl.

Drosera bulbosa Hook. ▷

△ *Drosera microphylla* Endl. . . . small-leaved sundew.

Here in Western Australia we have only two genera: *Aldrovandra* of the tropical Kimberley district, which grows in water and has leaves similar to those of *Dionaea,* and the genus *Drosera,* commonly called the sundews, of which we have 46 species.

Very appropriately *Drosera* takes its name from the Greek *droseros,* meaning dewy, for all the species possess hairs each with a knob-shaped tip from which is exuded a fluid that traps and digests insects, and it is this fluid in minute droplets which, in the slanting rays of the sun, gives an impression of dew formation. These hairs, furthermore, react to a stimulus imparted to the leaf by the touch of a fly or other small insect, and they then bend, a number of the hairs thus "pinning down" the insect.

The Western Australian species are famous for the variety of their growth and the colour of their blossoms.

Some are climbing plants which use their irritable hairs for this purpose; others are dwarf plants *(e.g. D. bulbosa)* with bulb-like organs deep in the soil and a rosette of leaves which lies on the surface; others possess the basal rosettes of leaves in addition to stem leaves, and one—*D. gigantea*—is quite stiff and erect, much branched, and this bears numerous

Drosera platystigma Lehm. . . . broad-stigma sundew. ▷

small white flowers. The shape of the leaf varies with the species: in some it is round and deeply concave, like a shallow cup; in others the leaf is heart-shaped and has two tails at the base, while in another the leaf is spoon-shaped. In some of the smallest species the leaves (together with their stipules) form a dense conical mass at the base of the flowering stem. The variability in the shape of the seeds is also interesting.

Turning now to the colours of the flowers, the difference—especially when compared with plants of this genus in other parts of the world—are most remarkable. Elsewhere the blossoms are usually white or red, but in this State there are climbing species with flowers of red, pink *(D. menziesii),* yellow or white *(D. macrantha).* The species which form small rosettes also have red, orange or white flowers, and the orange-red of these, as exemplified by *D. platystigma,* is of a hue and intensity not met with in other flowers. An outstandingly beautiful species is *D. microphylla,* which has purplish petals and emerald green sepals. One species *(D. indicta)* is found in the Kimberley and has long grass-like leaves: it grows in water.

It is a characteristic of *Drosera* that in the main they are to be found in damp sandy soils. The climbing species in particular grow on the open sandplains, while a large number—especially those with the orange-scarlet flowers—are to be found mainly in the vicinity of granite rocks where additional moisture, collecting from the rocks, is to be found.

Lauie's
Lookout
9/3

41

CEPHALOTACEAE

Pitcher plant family

CAPACITY to trap and digest insects is by no means restricted to the *Drosera* family for such plants are fairly numerous and belong to a number of different families. They are, however, better termed carnivorous than insectivorous since some (such as the bladderworts) appear to trap and digest only small crustaceans (shelled animals, mostly aquatic) while yet others have a wider choice of animal food.

Botanically these plants can be placed under two headings: first, there are those like the sundews which have the power of movement—by means of tentacles or folding leaves *(Drosera, Aldrovandra,* etc.); second, those which possess traps—such as the bladderworts *(Utricularia,* etc. and the pitcher plants) or those which have adhesive apparatus *(Byblis* and the like) and are called "flycatchers."

Of those which possess traps the Western Australian pitcher plant *(Cephalotus follicularis)* is one of the most remarkable and is world famous. It grows in moist spots, such as the banks of streams or the margins of swamps, and apparently requires free-moving soil water for its successful growth. In many respects it resembles the species of *Nepenthes* which are all tropical and usually climb by means of tendrils, which terminate in pitchers—much like those of *Cephalotus.*

Its range extends from near the Pallinup River westwards as far as Busselton, but it is only common between Albany and the Frankland River, in which area the best plants are to be seen.

This species develops a strong system of subterranean stems from which arise clusters, or rosettes, of leaves. The inner leaves of the cluster are the normal foliage leaves; green, flat and somewhat fleshy. The outer leaves are highly modified, for the leaf-stalk in its upper portion assumes the form of a tankard-like or pitcher-like vessel, surmounted by the small true leaf which forms the lid. This modified leaf-stalk or pitcher lies on the ground, and is broadest at the bottom. It is strengthened by three longitudinal

The West Australian pitcher plant *Cephalotus follicularis* Labill. ▷

girder-like winged structures, the middle one of which extends from the base almost to the orifice, is flat and two-edged above, and is provided with a few long soft hairs on its margins which act as a suitable ladder for ascent by insects. This, the front of the pitcher, is also curved upwards, which further facilitates insect movement.

Consideration of what occurs in other plants of similar structure (e.g. *Nepenthes)* leads one to assume that there is an attractive honey-like substance secreted in the pitcher, but this has not been observed. The insect visitor, upon reaching the top, drops into the internal cavity which contains an acid solution secreted from internal glands. Escape is rendered impossible by three obstacles; the very smooth concave inner surface, a projecting internal ledge close to the top and pointing downwards, and lastly a comb-like fringe of stiff, curved, inwards and downwards-pointing hard, sharp teeth which serve as a palisade. With such obstructions it is usually impossible for the smaller visitors to escape from the lethal pit. All but the harder parts of insects—beetle wing-cases, portions of ants—are digested by the plants.

The pitchers are of a pale green colour when fully grown, and their attraction is enhanced when the lower portion changes to a deep purple and the upper green area is veined blood-red. In addition the leafy portion, which forms the "lid" of the pitcher is rendered partially translucent by whitish patches which admit light to the interior.

It must be emphasised that the pitchers are in fact modified leaf-stalks.

One rarely sees the flowers of the pitcher plant,

for it blossoms in late summer, its small white flowers being like those of London Pride and arranged in panicles at the top of a very long stem.

BYBLIDACEAE

Byblis family

FORMERLY included among the sundews, *Byblis* is now regarded as belonging to a separate family with but one genus of only two species.

Both species occur in Western Australia—one in sandy spots in the South West, the other in swamps in the tropical north.

The plants can be recognised at once by the glandular hairs of their stems, which trap or imprison small insects (usually mosquitoes or small flies). They are stated to be carnivorous, having in this respect something of the characteristics of the sundews, although of a very different structure. The flowers differ essentially from the sundews in that *Byblis* have a two-chambered ovary and an undivided, oblique, style.

Byblis gigantea, the "rainbow plant" of the South West, has large purple-red flowers expanding to a diameter of nearly 50 mm. The plant grows to a height of about 600 mm, with rigid, upright stems and numerous thread-like leaves given off from near soil level. It is found in sandy soils, frequently wet in winter, and is common between the Murchison and Murray Rivers, more especially near the Hill, Moore and Canning Rivers.

The northern species, *B. liniflora,* has much smaller violet flowers, growing with a branching, straggling habit. It is found in the Kimberley division and as far south as the De Grey River.

△ The Rainbow Plant . . . *Byblis gigantea* Lindl.

△ The Chapman River bell-flower . . . *Billardiera ringens* (Drumm. et Harv.) E. M. Bennett.

△ *Billardiera erubescens* (Putterl.) E. M. Bennett . . . climbs on mallee or wattle.

△ *Billardiera bicolor* (Putterl.) E. M. Bennett . . . commonly known as the painted marianthus.

PITTOSPORACEAE

Pittosporum family

TWINING and climbing plants with flowers of singular attractiveness, which are members of the family *Pittosporaceae,* are a feature of the Western Australian flora of the South West, and it is to be regretted that one or two are now rare or almost extinct.

All of the family are woody-stemmed plants, native to the warmer regions of the earth, and particularly to Australia. There are nine genera and about 200 species.

Apart from the species of *Pittosporum*—which are the most widely distributed and may attain to tree proportions—the majority of these plants *(Billardiera, Sollya, Pronaya, Cheiranthera)* are small shrubs or climbers.

Pittosporum (which derives its name from two Greek words meaning pitch, and seed, in reference to the viscid seeds of plants of this genus) is represented locally by the shrub or tree popularly called native willow or cheesewood, for the inland form, found along watercourses, has drooping branches and the wood is soft and yellow. The coastal forms are mainly upright shrubs or small trees, with shorter and broader leaves than of those forms found in the interior.

The most popular species of the family belong to the genus *Billardiera,* which commemorates an explorer-botanist who visited these shores in 1792. Of these the orange-flowered Chapman River bell-flower *(Billardiera ringens)* deserves special comment. It is a plant with broad leathery leaves of a deep green, it carries clusters of orange flowers about 25 mm long with the petals ending in fine points. It was formerly common on the clay banks of that river but is now becoming scarce, although it occurs in other localities as well.

B. erubescens is another fine species with similar foliage but this is found in the interior and produces flowers of an intense red. It climbs on mallee or wattle in the eastern districts as far inland as Coolgardie, usually in granite country, and may reach a height of 4.5 metres. Among species found in the wheat-belt is the painted marianthus *(B. bicolor),* often low and somewhat shrubby in growth but sometimes a climber. This has white or pale yellow flowers striated with fine violet lines (hence the name pictus—painted). The white-flowered *B. candidus* is found in rocky places and is not uncommon near the Helena and Canning Rivers. Other species of the South West have blue flowers but are of less common occurrence.

Another most attractive species is the white-flowered *B. floribunda.* This is a common feature of the jarrah forest in the vicinity of Albany, flowering in December and January, but it extends northwards and may be found in shady spots as far away as the Helena River. Formerly common but now rare, *B latifolia* of the wheat country, is a climbing plant with rather broad leaves and two types of flowers on the same plant —lemon-yellow and burgundy-purple.

△ *Pronaya elegans* Hueg. . . . found in the sandplains at the foot of the Darling Range.

△ The Australian bluebell *Sollya heterophylla.* Lindl.

The Australian bluebell *(Sollya heterophylla)* is a common shrub or half-climber of the wandoo forest and woodland. Its intense blue flowers are in evidence throughout a great part of the spring and summer and the plant is widely cultivated.

Pronaya elegans is one of the latest blooming of the species of this family in the South West. It is not uncommon in the sandy soils near the coast and especially at the foot of the Darling Range. Its violet purple flowers are massed in dense clusters.

Other members of the family include the handsome species of *Cheiranthera* which extend far into the interior; these have flowers of a characteristic deep blue colour with yellow or orange-coloured anthers. Some are climbers, others are small shrubs, and with most species the blossoming continues into the summer months.

MIMOSACEAE

Acacia family

△ Jam wattle . . . *Acacia acuminata* Benth.

THE 350 species of *Mimosaceae* in Western Australia are rather more than half the number occurring in the world, and although the wattles—the more usual name—are not particularly Australian, it is in this continent, and especially in south-western Australia, that they have evinced themselves in a bewildering assortment of forms.

The Acacia family—one of three which constitute the legumes, plants which have pods—is characterised by regular or symmetrical flowers, never solitary, collected in round heads or in spikes. The sepals and petals of these do not overlap but are joined in the bud by their margins, the stamens usually being very numerous, thus imparting to the flower-head or spike its "fluffy" appearance.

However, of the 30 genera of the *Mimosaceae* made up of 1500 species, the greater number are species of *Acacia* and *Mimosa,* the latter including the sensitive plant *(M. pudica)* common in the old-world tropics. The name, Mimosa, is often given to the common black wattle of Victoria. In Europe it is cultivated for its fragrance.

Dealing with the 350 Western Australian species, these are almost all species of *Acacia,* the

△ About ten species of Acacia are called mulga. This one, in the Gibson Desert, is *Acacia aneura* F.Muell.

exceptions being *Dichrostachys* of the North West, *Neptunia* (the sensitive plant of the Kimberley), *Albizia* of the Kimberley and the South West—more commonly known as the swamp wattle—and *Pithecellobium,* a handsome tree of the far north. The mesquite *(Prosopis)* and *Leucaena* both introduced from America, also belong to this family.

Acacias are found throughout the State, from the feathery-leaved species of the karri forest *(A. pentadenia* and *A. gilbertii)* to those of the far inland desert, and they undergo strange modifications in response to the changes in climate.

The forms of the drier, inland country (such as jam tree and mulga) are all leafless. Only in the

Karri wattle *Acacia pentadenia* Lindl. in tingle tingle forest near Nornalup, on the south coast. ▷

far north, in the Kimberley, do we again encounter feathery-leaved wattles, mostly spiny. Yet leafless species—with leaf-like leaf-stalks—occupy every type of country from the wet forest areas of the South West and the river flats of the Kimberley into the heart of the continent. This type of *Acacia* is limited to Australia and a few adjacent islands in the Pacific; otherwise this large genus, found throughout the warm regions of all continents, is characterised by pinnate leaves. In Africa we find *Acacia* formations extending from the Sudan into Rhodesia, and these are of the type known as "camel thorns." A similar climatic type in Western Australia is seen in mulga bush country, where the mulga trees (wattles) form almost the entire larger woody growth. About ten species are collectively known as mulga—minnie-ritchie (fibrous barked plants) and curara (needle-leaved plants)—all of which have a distinct value as top-feed or browsing plants, valuable for the foliage of many and for the seeds of all, and especially the bogada bush which bears long pendulous pods, somewhat resembling old-fashioned tallow candles.

A few species of *Acacia* are quite leafless, the green stems functioning as leaves. Some of these are found in the interior, others in the South West.

Another group of the genus, and this is restricted to the South West, includes those species which have winged stems and vertical teeth, or phyllodes. One of these, *A. diptera* is common in the shady woods. Related to this is *A. alata* which, though leafless, is only found in shady spots on the banks of streams. The common prickly Moses *(A. pulchella),* a corruption of "prickly mimosa,"

△ This specimen of Dunn's Wattle, *Acacia dunnii* (Maiden) Turrill., grows on a river flat in the north Kimberley.

△ The common prickly Moses . . . *Acacia pulchella* R.Br.

48

△ Blackboys and *Acacia decipiens* R.Br. on the highlands above Augusta, in the south-west corner of the State.

is a spiny shrub with small feathery leaves which covers the hills of the Darling Range with gold during spring months.

In the lower South West *A. decipiens* often provides a convenient support for the climbing coral vine, *Kennedia coccinea*.

The greatest variety of species, nevertheless, is to be found in the shrublands of the wheat-belt, where broom-like or needle-leaf plants, which remain unnoticed for the greater part of the year, come into blossom in the spring in such magnificence that they appear as large masses of gold which all but conceal the foliage.

As a further aid to recognition it can be said that the leaves of *Mimosaceae* are always divided and fern-like, i.e. they are composed of leaflets which are arranged in a feather-type form, as in

the Cootamundra wattle or the common Victorian black wattle, already referred to. Where, in many species of *Acacia*, the leaves do not appear to be of this type, but simple and undivided, they are not the true leaves but flattened leaf-stalks. In this respect it is interesting to watch the development of the seedling plant, which first produces the compound feather-like (bipinnate) leaves on a slender stalk. The subsequent leaves show, in such wattles, a continuance of this type of leaf for a number of pairs, but the main leaf-stalk becomes broader with each successive pair until the leaflets finally disappear and only the flattened leaf-stalk is produced. When such wattles are damaged and produce sucker leaves or coppice shoots, we find once more a reversion to the compound leaf for a time in the young shoots.

CAESALPINIACEAE

Cassia family

△ *Petalostylis labicheoides* R.Br. . . . a typical **Cassia** flower with over-lapping petals, the top one inside.

THIS is a family that includes a West African tree of which the bark is poisonous and is used by the native tribes in ceremonies of "ordeal" and as an arrow poison. It is the second family of legumes and includes those pod-bearing plants of which the flowers are not small, or crowded into heads or spikes (as with *Acacia),* nor are they pea-flowered. Instead the flowers are of the *Cassia* type—irregular or, at most, almost regular, with overlapping petals of which the uppermost is inside—note, inside—the remainder. Familiar examples are the species of *Cassia,* of *Poinciana, Bauhinia, Erythrophloeum,* and *Parkinsonia.* The Royal Poinciana *(Delonix regia)* from Madagascar also belongs to the family, which includes 80 genera and numerous species, most of which are indigenous to tropical America.

In Western Australia the related genera comprise *Erythrophloeum, Labichea, Petalostylis, Cassia, Lysiphyllum* and *Caesalpinia.*

Of these *Erythrophloeum* is represented by the single species *E. chlorostachys,* a tree of the

Labichea lanceolata Benth. . . .

common in the Darling Range. ▷

tropical areas northwards from the De Grey River. It is the well known ironwood of the Kimberley, and is toxic to animals. (This is a tree closely related to the African species already referred to, *E. guineense,* the red-water tree of Sierra Leone.)

A common tree in the tropics is the *Bauhinia (Lysiphyllum cunninghamii).* Often known by the corrupt name "Bohemia tree," it is small, has dull red flowers in fair abundance which are succeeded by large purple pods. Like so many other plants of the region where it grows, it is deciduous.

Labichea is entirely southern in habitat: *L. cassioides* is common in the Murchison district and has compound leaves with sharply pointed leaflets. *L. lanceolata* and *L. punctata* are found farther south, both being common in the Darling Range; the former is a shrub bearing yellow flowers with red-spotted petals, and pungent-pointed leaves, while the latter is an under-shrub with broad, obtuse leaves and pale yellow, unspotted, blossoms.

Natives of the north and the desert interior are the species of *Petalostylis. P. labicheoides* is a handsome yellow-flowered shrub with erect twiggy branches, and is to be seen in the Kimberley, while *P. millefolium* is found in the red sand of the desert as far south as Comet Vale. This latter species has rich yellow flowers on prostrate stems and the numerous leaflets are grey and hairy.

The remaining genus, *Cassia,* contains 25 local species and none of these is found in the lower South West. The greater number are inhabitants of the tropics, the mulga country and the desert, and are, in the main, plants with grey, hairy or hoary leaves. Exceptions are a few attractive and large flowered species confined to the tropical north, such as *C. venusta* and the remarkable *C. magnifolia* with very large leaves, which is restricted to the stony soils around Hall's Creek and a few places along the Fitzroy River. The

△ Wild senna *Cassia pleurocarpa* F. Muell., a species which grows far inland.

PAPILIONACEAE
Pea family

THE third of the families of legumes is the Pea family, and, apart from being one of the largest families of flowering plants, it is of great economic importance for it provides many articles of food (peas, lentils, peanuts, beans and soy beans), of fodder (clovers, trefoils, vetches, lupins, etc.), oils, gums and resins. It comprises over 300 genera and very numerous species generally distributed over the temperate and tropical regions of the earth, of which 50 genera with about 500 species are to be found in Western Australia, chiefly in the South West. The plants range from trees and shrubs to climbers and herbs.

The members of the family are quite easily recognised by reason of the shape of the flowers of the differing species, all of which bear a fancied resemblance to a butterfly—hence the name *Papilionaceae,* from the Latin *papilio,* a butterfly.

A glance round any ordinary garden will disclose numerous representatives under cultivation, but in Western Australia its importance stems from the fact that a number of the indigenous species are poisonous to stock. For example, there are the pea-flowered poisons *(Gastrolobium* and *Oxylobium),* the lamb poisons *(Isotropis),* the rattle-pods *(Crotalaria* of the north) and some others. (For an account of all of these see *The Toxic Plants of Western Australia: Gardner and Bennetts: published by West Australian Newspapers Ltd.)*

Plainly, with such a wealth of material, selection is difficult and the examples given here are but representative of the very large number of wildflowers of the Pea family to be found in this State.

species which extends farthest south is *C. eremophila,* a small shrub with deep yellow blossoms and compound leaves reduced to needle-like leaflets.

Among the more attractive of the inland species is that called wild senna *(C. pleurocarpa)* found growing far into the centre of the continent. As it extends farther westward it improves in stature and the leaflets become broader as the climate conditions improve. It is found from the Gascoyne River southwards to the Eastern Goldfields and then westward again to Dalwallinu, Mullewa and Carrabin, and has been seen at Kellerberrin. (Its seed is probably disseminated by birds for it does not appear to be permanent under the climatic conditions of the wheat-belt.) The plant contains the same principle as the sennas of commerce (hence its common name) and the pods are equally efficacious as a purgative, but the same principle is sometimes responsible for mortalities in stock, especially in young animals which eat too freely of the foliage and pods.

Gompholobium knightianum Lindl. . . . a typical pea. ▷

△ Bacon-and-eggs *Oxylobium capitatum* Benth.

△ *Mirbelia dilatata* R.Br.

PEA FAMILY

A common diffuse shrub occurring on the coastal plain between the Murchison and Vasse rivers is bacon-and-eggs *(Oxylobium capitatum)* also to be found on the south coast to the east of Albany. It flowers from August to October.

Oxylobium linearifolium favours situations close to watercourses or pools where the soil is moist. It is an erect weak-stemmed shrub from 1.8 to 2.5 metres tall growing in dense thickets of other shrubs. Found between the Murchison River and King George Sound, it is noticeably common between the Canning and Preston Rivers and blossoms in spring and early summer.

Much smaller is *Chorizema aciculare* which, rarely exceeding 300 mm in height, has a wide area of distribution between the Swan River and the south coast. The most attractive forms are those with scarlet or pink flowers found in the vicinity of the Stirling Range. The sharp, needle-like leaves of this species are noteworthy.

Favouring a very different situation is *Mirbelia seorsifolia,* a small shrub of the Eastern Goldfields. Found in red sandy soil between Campion and Coolgardie and southwards to Norseman, it can make a particularly attractive picture when flowering in September and October.

The common lamb-poison *(Isotropis cuneifolia)* is very common between the Murchison River and the south coast and is always found in sandy soil. Flowering from August until late in October, the south-western species of *Isotropis* can always be recognised by the deep purple striations on the back of the standard, which extend from the base to the margin.

▽ Common lamb-poison *Isotropis cuneifolia* (Sm.) Domin.

△ *Chorizema aciculare* (D.C.) C. A. Gardn. is common in the South West.

▽ *Chorizema cordatum* Lindl. and *Kennedia coccinea* Vent.

△ *Burtonia villosa* Meisn., an attractive shrub which grows only between the Stirling Ranges and Albany.

There are 26 species of *Gompholobium* and *Burtonia,* some of which are very handsome. The botanical difference between the two is only in the number of ovules in the ovary—two in *Burtonia* and four or more in *Gompholobium:* there is, however, considerable variation in the leaf forms. Perhaps the two most attractive plants are shrubs from 300 mm to 2.5 metres in height— *Burtonia scabra* and *B. villosa.* The first-named may be seen in many sandy spots in the Swan River area and has a glabrous calyx and ovary: the latter is found only between Albany and the Stirling Range and this has a silky calyx and ovary. *Gompholobium burtonioides* is a small shrub, rarely exceeding 200 mm when fully grown and the clear yellow flowers occur in dense masses.

Stinkwood is the name given to some species of *Jacksonia,* especially *J. sternbergiana.* The genus consists of leafless plants or, at most, they possess leaves only in the young stage of growth and what may appear to be leaves are flattened stems, or cladodes, which have flowers on their margins. *J. floribunda,* however, has its flowers otherwise, these being borne in dense racemes which arise below the large cladodes. This shrub attains a height of three metres or more and is frequently found growing in the white sandy plains adjoining the Swan River.

▽ Common near Perth, *Burtonia scabra* R.Br.

▽ *Jacksonia sternbergiana* Hueg., often called stinkwood.

53

△ *Daviesia incrassata* Sm. flowers in winter and spring throughout the South West.

△ Handsome wedge-pea *Gompholobium venustum* R.Br.

The species of *Sphaerolobium* number 12 and, with one exception, are confined to south-western Australia. In general they may be recognised by the standard of the flower which is red with a yellow base and frequently green-spotted. *S. alatum* is peculiar in having yellow flowers with winged stems. This is found only in the districts around King George Sound and is not uncommon on the stony heights of the Stirling Range, flowering in October.

A plant which is exceptionally distinctive in appearance is the little known shrub locally called the staghorn bush *(Daviesia epiphylla)*. In the absence of leaves the stems become remarkably flattened and divided upwards like the fronds of the staghorn fern, but are of a blue-grey colour and are notably tough and rigid. The handsome coral-pink or scarlet pea-shaped flowers are produced in clusters which arise from the flat surface of the stems. To be found in gravelly

soils in a few very restricted localities, none distant from the Hill River district, it flowers in early summer. Of the 52 species of the genus in Western Australia, *D. incrassata* is a common representative, being met with throughout the South West, where it can be seen flowering in winter and spring. The colour of the flowers (orange-scarlet) is typical of the greater number of the *Daviesias* and the blossoms are succeeded by triangular leg-of-mutton-shaped pods which are the main characteristic of this genus.

The staghorn bush *Daviesia epiphylla* Meisn. has △ ◁ remarkable flattened stems which look like leaves.

△ The purple of *Hovea elliptica* (Sm.) D.C., the yellow of *Bossiaea laidlawiana* Tovey & Morris and blue *Orthrosanthus multifolorus* Sm. brighten the forest in Piano Gully, between Manjimup and Pemberton.

There are 43 species of *Gastrolobium* indigenous to Western Australia; of these 28 are toxic and these, with one exception, are found in the temperate areas. The exception is the wallflower poison *(G. grandiflorum)* of the stony hills of the Hamersley Range, the King Leopold Range and of the country to the north. Of the southern species, breelya *(G. laytonii)* extends into the mulga country but 41 species are strictly confined to the South West. Crinkle-leaved poison *(G. villosum)* is a common diffuse undershrub of the gravelly soils of the Darling Range, flowering in September and October. The blossoms of all of the species are yellow, rarely red, but often yellow suffused with red.

In all of the examples of *Papilionaceae* so far referred to the flowers have ten separate and distinct stamens, but in the following the stamens are either all united, or nine of them are united and the tenth (uppermost) stamen is free.

The genus *Bossiaea* has in general yellow and brown, or purple, flowers and in Western Australia is represented by 20 species. Of these *B.*

△ Water bush *Bossiaea aquifolium* Benth.

△ Crinkle-leaved poison *Gastrolobium villosum* Benth.

▽ *Gastrolobium appressum* C. A. Gardn.

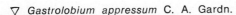

△ *Daviesia cordata* Sm.

△ Tree hovea, *Hovea elliptica* (Sm.) D.C., grows in the karri forests.

△ *Templetonia retusa* (Vent.) R.Br., the most attractive member of the *Templetonia* species.

biloba is a small shrub or undershrub with characteristic foliage. It is widely distributed from the Murchison River to the south coast but is nowhere abundant except perhaps on the gravelly clay soils of the Darling Range.

Six species of *Templetonia* are found in this State, all very dissimilar in appearance. The kerosene bush *(T. sulcata)* of the woodlands in the agricultural districts is a leafless shrub with yellow or purple flowers. The most attractive and the largest flowered species is *T. retusa* which is a conspicuous shrub of the limestone coastal areas

from Shark Bay to the Great Australian Bight, but on the south coast it occurs on granitic soils. The large dull red flowers are produced in July and continue until October.

Blossoms of an intense violet colour which place them among the most attractive of our wildflowers are carried by the genus *Hovea*. It contains 11 species of which six are confined to Western Australia. With the exception of a small spinescent form common around Kalgoorlie, the remaining five have a south-western habitat. The best known, undoubtedly, is *H. trisperma,* much in evidence around Perth, but the equally attractive needle-leaved Hovea *(H. pungens)* is similarly common. The holly-leaved Hovea *(H. chorizemifolia)* is most usually found in the gravelly soils of the Darling Range and has, perhaps, the richest hued flowers of any of the species. It gained its common name by reason of the undulate prickly-margined leaves. *H. elliptica* is the tree hovea, a shrub often 4.5 metres tall and found exclusively in the karri forest, while *H. stricta* is found in two localities only—the sandy country of the Vasse River district and the sandplains northwards from Dandaragan and the Hill River.

△ *Hovea trisperma* Benth. Is the best known hovea.

△ The holly-leaved Hovea, *Hovea chorizemifolia* (Sweet) D.C., is usually found in the gravel soils of the Darling Range.

△ The green bird-flower *Crotalaria cunninghamii* R.Br. is found in sandy creek beds in the North West.

Crotalaria crassipes is a representative of a genus of which the species are called rattle-pods—by reason of the shell or parchment-like pods in which the seeds rattle when ripe; in fact, the name is derived from the Greek *crotalon*, a rattle or castanet. There are 16 species of the genus in Western Australia, by far the greater number of which are found north of the Fitzroy River. *C. crassipes* is an annual plant found in a few localities in the Kimberley district where it grows to a height of three metres in a season, the trunk-like stem being woody and the large leaves and massive spikes of flowers render it attractive during the period February to May. It is closely related to *C. retusa*, a plant which causes 'walkabout' disease in horses, and to the green bird-flower *(C. cunninghamii)*, found in the sand along the north-west coast and in the sandy beds of water-courses. The handsome *C. laburnifolia* of our gardens is also indigenous to the Prince Regent River district.

◁ *Crotalaria crassipes* Hook. is an annual in the far north which grows three metres in a season.

△ The striking Sturt Pea, *Clianthus formosus* (G.Don.) Ford & Vickery, is found throughout the northern and central areas of the continent. Dampier first collected it on the north west coast.

PEA FAMILY

The very striking Sturt Pea *(Clianthus formosus)* is the one species of this genus—there are but two in all—native to Australia. It is found throughout the northern and central areas of the continent, extending south as far as Lake Lefroy but is most common between the Cane and De Grey Rivers and at Point Samson on the northwest coast. It is of interest to note in passing that, although this plant commemorates the name of Sturt the explorer, it was included in the first collection made of Australian plants—by Dampier, who collected it on the north-west coast. It occurs in two forms: one is prostrate and the other is semi-erect, with a deep clear claret-coloured boss in place of the more common black boss. This erect form is confined to the country around the Hamersley Range and Nullagine River.

Widespread and eye-catching, the Sturt Pea is probably the best known member of the Pea family.

A climbing plant, flowering in spring and native to the South West is the coral vine *(Kennedia coccinea)*. One of the 11 local species of the genus *Kennedia,* it is common in the South West especially in the jarrah forest. Its relative, the scarlet runner *(K. prostrata)* is a common creeping plant also of the coastal area yet this, too, is found more than 300 km inland on the sandy banks of creeks or on the margins of springs. The black and gold species seen at Cape Riche, *K. nigricans,* and the forage plant, *K. stirlingii,* are among the better known of the remainder, although the most handsome of all is *K. beckxiana* from the Israelite Bay area.

Yet another climbing plant of the South West is the wild wistaria *(Hardenbergia comptoniana)* sometimes called wild sarsaparilla. The solitary species of the genus in Western Australia is widely known in cultivation elsewhere, principally in Mozambique and Madagascar. Under cultivation it is very rewarding, being quite hardy and

△ Wild wistaria, *Hardenbergia comptoniana* (Andr.) Benth., a South West climber, is widely cultivated.

extremely attractive when in flower. In September and October it becomes one of the features of the sandy coastal bush country between the Swan River and King George Sound.

As to the family's botanical characteristics: the five petals are not all alike; at the back of the flower is the (usually) large rounded erect petal called the standard. Inside this are two wing petals which in turn enclose the innermost two united petals which are termed the keel—which encloses ten stamens and the ovary, which later develops into a pod. There are but few departures from this type, exceptions being in the local *Brachysema* and *Jansonia,* the latter being restricted to the Augusta-Margaret River district. In these the standard petals are often very small.

▽ The coral vine, *Kennedia coccinea* Vent., is common in the South West, especially in the jarrah forests.

▽ The scarlet runner, *Kennedia prostrata* R.Br., is common on the coast, but also occurs, on creek banks, 300 km inland.

△ The coral vine *Kennedia coccinea* Vent. provides splashes of red in this section of bush on high land near
the golf course above Augusta. The wattle is *Acacia decipiens* R.Br. and the banksia *B. grandis* Willd.

GERANIACEAE

Geranium family

WHEN considering the Geranium family—of which there are but 11 genera consisting of 850 species distributed over the temperate and sub-tropical regions of the earth—it is as well for the reader to bear in mind that the plants cultivated in gardens and commonly called geraniums and pelargoniums are in the main all species of *Pelargonium.* Besides these species and other numerous species which ornament the hedgerows and fields of Europe, there are those species—chiefly of Mediterranean origin—which are now common weeds of the cultivated lands of south-western Australia, as are also the pink-flowered species of *Erodium,* known as cranesbill.

The indigenous plants of Western Australia are species of *Pelargonium* and the blue-flowered species of *Erodium:* all of the others have been introduced.

The common native so-called wild geranium is in fact a cranesbill *(Erodium cygnorum).* Formerly this had a very extensive range from the Swan River into the far interior of the State. Its flowers are delicate in texture, are of a light, though somewhat dull, blue or rarely lilac and the plants vary considerably according to the available moisture. The largest specimens are those found in mulga country where, in good winter seasons, the plants carpet the soil and attain a height of nearly 600 mm, whereas under dry conditions the plants remain diminutive.

The native pelargoniums are five in number and the finest of these is the diminutive *P. havlasae* which grows in a few places between Tammin and the Stirling Range. It rarely exceeds 100 mm in height and its delicately perfumed white flowers arise from a rosette of scented, geranium-like leaves. It flowers from June to November and when growing in stony country it has an especially attractive appearance. The commonest species is *P. capitatum* which is found in limestone country of the west coast, particularly between Perth and the Vasse River.

Pelargonium havlasae Domin. rarely exceeds 100 mm in ▷ height, has delicately scented flowers.

△ The common *Pelargonium capitatum* (L.) Ait. probably came from Africa originally.

Plants of this family are easily recognisable by their flowers and fruits. The flowers have five green sepals, five distinct petals, and 10 stamens —all of which, or only five of them, bear anthers. The most characteristic feature, however, is the fruit which consists of an elongated fleshy axis arising from the centre of the flower and produced into a long point.

In cranesbills these become spiralled in the lower part like a corkscrew: the upper part bends away at right angles. After falling to the ground the carpel may be held in an upright position by surrounding grass, with the corkscrewed portion downwards and the seed-point touching the soil. Then under the action of moisture the twisted portion begins to uncoil. The right angled part engages across the upright stems of grass and the uncoiling results in the seed burying itself in the soil, almost exactly like the seeds of corkscrew grasses.

RUTACEAE

Boronia family

UNEXPECTED though it may be to some readers, the attractively perfumed *Boronias* are members of the same family *(Rutaceae)* as the orange and lemon, lime, cumquat and other citrus fruits. All have the aromatic attribute which is one of the characteristics of the family, species of which are generally rich in oil. In fact, the name *Rutaceae* is derived from rue *(Ruta graveolens),* a herb native to Southern Europe, which was formerly grown extensively in gardens for its aromatic and medicinal qualities. Members of this family can usually be recognised by the fact that in Australia they are all shrubs or trees, often with small oil dots in their foliage.

In Western Australia the main representation is in the southern part of the State and in the tropical north.

Best known are the species of *Boronia, Crowea, Diplolaena*—inaptly called the native rose—and the local hazel, *Chorilaena,* of the karri forest.

The most widespread genus is, without doubt, *Boronia* (with 48 species) which is common

△ *Boronia megastigma* Nees., the common scented Boronia, grows in the winter swamp lands of the South West.

△ *Boronia ovata* Lindl.

◁ *Boronia cymosa* Endl. . . . granite Boronia.

62

△ *Boronia thymifolia* Turcz.

△ *Boronia pulchella* Turcz., a variety found in the Stirling Ranges.

throughout the South West, while a few species are found at higher altitudes in the tropical north. The scented boronia *(B. megastigma)* with flowers of a rich chocolate brown outside and greenish-yellow inside, is undoubtedly the most popular. Its scent is of such intensity that at close range it is frequently undetected, for the strength of its perfume affects the olfactory nerves. It is found in winter swamp land of the South West, mainly in the karri forest and southern limits of the jarrah forest, and flowers in July and August. At least one other species, *B. purdieana,* (also yellow-flowered), is heavily scented: it is found in sandy soils near Perth. It, too, flowers early in the winter but, unlike *B. megastigma,* grows in dry sand. Other species have yellow, blue, white, pink (for example, *B. cymosa* and *B. heterophylla)* red or purple blossoms, and some extend eastwards to the Goldfields.

△ *Boronia alata* Sm.

△ *Boronia heterophylla* F.Muell.

△ Bush Crowea, *Crowea dentata* (R.Br.) Benth. occurs in karri forests.

△ Pepper-and-salt *Eriostemon spicatus* A.Rich.

△ *Boronia fastigiata* Bartl.

◁ *Diplolaena grandiflora* Desf. thrives in the red coastal sands between Geraldton and Shark Bay.

Of *Crowea* there are two main forms, both of which grow in the higher rainfall districts of the south. *C. angustifolia var. dentata,* usually about three metres in height, is found in the karri forest, and a smaller form *C. angustifolia,* rarely exceeding 600 mm, is found in swamps. Both flower in August, September and October.

Ten species of *Eriostemon* are indigenous to Western Australia and these are commonly called pepper-and-salt plants. One of the most attractive is *E. spicatus.* It grows as tall as 600 mm and its slender spikes of tiny pinkish-lavender coloured, star-like flowers may be seen in the spring in the sandy soils of the western coastal plain.

In *Diplolaena* (a genus containing six species) the numerous insignificant flowers are crowded into heads surrounded by petal-like bracts, the whole resembling a single flower. An example is *D. grandiflora* which grows in red sand near the coast between Geraldton and Shark Bay. *D. angustifolia* is a much handsomer species, however, and is to be found in the Yanchep district near Perth.

The local hazels *(Chorilaena)* are shrubs of the karri forest and are found between Manjimup and Albany. These somewhat resemble *Diplolaena* but have broad, coarsely-hairy, lobed leaves, and the

△ The native rose, *Diplolaena angustifolia* Hook., grows in the Yanchep area, north of Perth.

inflorescence remains a greenish-yellow.

The species of *Phebalium* are most common in dry country but the blister bush *(P. argenteum)* grows in swamps to a height of a metre in the South West as far north as Perth. It should be remarked that this plant frequently causes skin trouble in persons who come in contact with its silvery, scurfy leaves.

Somewhat resembling *Phebalium* are the species of *Microcybe* and *Asterolasia*. None of these is very common and they have a very restricted range. The flowers are usually white, but in *Asterolasia* there is one yellow-flowered species and one pink.

In the sandplain country of the Irwin district one of the most striking plants is *Geleznowia calycina* which flowers in September and October. What appears to be a single flower is usually a cluster of two or three surrounded by yellow or orange-brown and yellow, *Pimelea*-like bracts which almost conceal the blossom.

Finally, among the least known members of the *Boronia* family is a species of *Microcitrus* which grows in the north-west Kimberley and bears a small orange, and the sheep bush *(Geijera lineari-folia)* which is found in the Norseman-Balladonia area.

Dealing with the family as a whole the flowers have four or five sepals, usually united in the lower part; a similar number of petals; a similar number of stamens—or twice the number, in which case the alternate stamens are different from the others or sterile; and a distinct disc or fleshy ring between the stamens and the ovary which is usually lobed. The fruit is either fleshy, or dry and separating into distinctly free parts or almost free parts.

Nematolepis phebalioides Turcz. . . . another member of ▷ the Boronia family.

9/3 Baljinegan △ *Boronia ramosa* (Lindl.) Benth. Blue

△ Orange-brown and yellow bracts almost conceal the blossom of this *Geleznowia verrucosa* Turcz.

TREMANDRACEAE

Tremandra family

THIS is a family entirely restricted to southern Australia. There are about 30 species arranged under three genera—*Tremandra, Platytheca* and *Tetratheca*—and the first two are confined to the south west of Western Australia.

The common species of *Platytheca (P. verticillata)* rarely exceeds 300 mm in height and has its narrow, needle-like leaves crowded at intervals along the stems.

Both of the species of *Tremandra* are restricted to the country between King George Sound and the northern confines of the karri forest. They are shrubs with rather broad, toothed, opposite leaves and grow in dense shade. The flowers are a rich blue.

The genus *Tetratheca* enjoys a much wider range of climate and soil conditions. It has no common name. In all there are about 27 species found in different parts of Australia and of these 13 species are native to Western Australia. These native species have flowers of red, pink or white, and, although growing mainly in the jarrah or karri forests, it is remarkable that there are two leafless but not unattractive species found in the dry eastern interior not far from Southern Cross: both of these have pink flowers of a daintiness which seems out of place in their arid natural environment. Another leafless species, *T. nuda,* is found in the Darling Range but the remaining 10 species are leafy plants. *T. viminea* is a shrub which grows up to 450 mm in height, is found in the shady woods of the Darling Range between the Swan River and the Blackwood and Vasse Rivers, and flowers in August and September.

△ *Tetratheca setigera* Endl.

△ *Tetratheca viminea* Lindl. . . . slender Tetratheca.

The flowers of all *Tetrathecas* are borne on slender stalks which are sometimes elongated and this gives these plants an appearance of delicacy not often noticeable in Western Australian flora.

All the members of this family are shrubs, the flowers of which have four or five sepals and the same number of petals. The stamens are twice the number of the petals and the usually deeply coloured anthers are contracted into a long, narrow point and open in a single terminal pore. The ovary is usually bilocular.

◁ *Platytheca verticillata* (Hueg.) Baill., the common Platytheca (left) and *Tetratheca hispidissima* Steetz.

POLYGALACEAE

Milkweed family

THE Milkweed family is important because (among other reasons) it provides two very useful drugs: the senega, or snake-root *(Polygala senega)* of the United States, used widely in lung disorders, and the rhatany root *(Krameria triandra)* of South America, an astringent used in throat complaints.

There are 10 genera and about 700 species included in *Polygalaceae,* which are widely distributed over the globe, except in New Zealand and the polar regions.

The few native Western Australian species of *Polygala* are found in Kimberley, while species of *Comesperma* are confined to the South West. The milkweeds of the north are herbs growing in wet situations and generally have blue flowers.

Comespermas are in the main small shrubs, usually of elegant appearance, but three are twining plants. Of the latter *C. volubile* has very few small leaves but carries large masses of sky-blue

△ *Comesperma virgatum* Labill. . . . racemes of flowers at the end of wand-like stems.

blossoms in September. It is common in the gravelly soils extending from Wongan Hills to Merredin and southwards to the coast. Another climbing species, *C. integerrimum,* bears purple and yellow flowers. One of the commonest shrubs of this genus is the Swan River broom *(C. scoparium)* which is found in gravelly or gravelly-sandy soil in the Northampton area, southwards to Ravensthorpe and eastwards to Tammin. *C. acerosum* is a small spiny shrub with purple-pink flowers, and *C. flavum* is a small slender species carrying pale yellow flowers, common in the Albany district yet extending northwards to the Murchison River, where, however, it is rare except in low-lying, sandy, sub-swampy spots. *C. calymega* is not infrequent in the sandy areas between Perth and Busselton, while *C. confertum* is widely distributed in the western and southern coastal areas from Mogumber to Albany and along the south coast. It flowers in October, November and December, attaining a height of from 300 to 600 mm.

◁ The Love Creeper . . . *Comesperma volubile* Labill. . . . a common twining plant of the South West.

STACKHOUSIACEAE

Stackhousia family

By far the most attractive species are those which have a slender erect habit and carry racemes of purple-red or magenta flowers at the end of wand-like, leafy stems. A number of them centre around *C. virgatum* which is common in swampy or low-lying, sandy, winter-wet soils between the Hill River and the south coast. Indeed, it is this species, and the closely related *C. nudiusculum,* so common around Albany and Mount Barker, and flowering for the entire spring and late into summer, which make the genus popular.

The most familiar garden plants of this family are, however, species of *Polygala,* one of which *(P. myrtifolia)* is a well known shrub with small oblong leaves and rather large magenta-purple flowers, notable locally for its capacity to thrive in poor soils under conditions of little moisture. It is equally at home in the dry interior or in the poor sand of the coast.

For recognition purposes it is well to remember that the flowers of this family superficially resemble the Pea flower, but the standard petal is not developed as such, the eight stamens are attached to a petal-like sheath, with the anthers attached by their bases and opening at the apex in pores. The fruit is two-chambered and each chamber has, as a rule, one pendulous seed with an appendage (aril) at one end. The seeds are commonly hairy.

R ESTRICTED to Australia, New Zealand, and the Philippines this family has only two genera—*Stackhousia* with 19 species, and *Macgregoria,* with a single species confined to the interior of Western Australia and central Australia. Eight species of *Stackhousia* occur in Western Australia. All the plants of this genus are herbaceous, with a number of stems arising from a rootstock and the flowers are white or yellow, and arranged in elongated spikes.

S. huegelii has a strong hyacinth fragrance when in blossom, which adds considerably to its charm. It is often common in the moist soil around granite rocks in the interior, flowering in the months of August and September. The coastal forms of this plant are often found in sandy swampy places, but in such situations they have not the delightful perfume of the forms found close to granite rocks. Its range extends from the Murchison River to the south coast between Albany and Bremer Bay, flowering from July to September. Other species, such as *S. dielsii,* not uncommon in the Ajana district, have yellow flowers. *S. dielsii* is entirely leafless when in flower, and its spikes of rich yellow flowers on their rush-like stems are singularly attractive. Another yellow-flowered species is *S. brunonis,* which has a three-winged hop-like fruit, also yellow. This species has a black-flowered form.

Apart from *S. huegelii,* the only other common white-flowered species in the South West is *S. pubescens,* which can readily be distinguished by the downy axis of the flowering spike.

The species of *Stackhousia* are easily recognised by their habit of growth—a perennial root-stock from which several stems arise, the narrow, often crowded leaves of the lower part of the stem, the flowers in spikes; a small five-lobed green calyx, and a tubular corolla with five spreading lobes at the top, the five unequal stamens, and the ovary divided into from two to five nut-like bodies, each of which is one-seeded, and not splitting for the dispersal of these seeds.

◁ *Stackhousia huegelii* Endl. has a strong hyacinth fragrance when it flowers, in August-September.

SAPINDACEAE

Soapberry family

△ Native hops . . . *Dodonaea attenuata* A.Cunn.

OF the 1,000 or so species, comprising some 125 genera, which constitute the Soapberry family—an important one in its tropical distribution—are such plants as the leechee, or litchi (*Litchi chinensis*) and the Korean golden-rain tree (*Koelreuteria paniculata*).

In Western Australia are to be found seven genera, five of which are tropical or native to the warmer, arid regions of the interior. Of the seven the more important are *Cardiospermum, Dodonaea, Diplopeltis, Heterodendron* and *Atalaya.*

The best known of the genus *Cardiospermum* is the balloon vine (*C. halicacabum*), a straggling or climbing plant with three-lobed leaves and white irregular flowers, which are followed by an inflated three-cell fruit containing three large globular black seeds.

Native hops belong to *Dodonaea,* a genus widely dispersed over almost all hot countries, yet in Western Australia some of the 33 species extend to the south coast. Most of these are shrubs of attractive appearance although the flowers are small and very insignificant. It is the coloured inflated fruits which form the attraction of these plants, and since these remain for long periods, some species are worthy of much wider cultivation in gardens. *D. attenuata* is already in cultivation, and this has forms with dull purplish foliage, but other species also merit attention, and such have broadly winged, hop-like fruits, of which some are a brilliant red or purple, others yellow or brown.

Besides the typical form with the winged hop-like fruit, there are those species of which the fruits are winged only in the upper half, the wings standing outward and upward and giving an elegant appearance. Then there are those which have the wings reduced to flat, crescent-shaped appendages at the summit of the inflated fruits, and, furthermore, those which have merely conical excrescences. The foliage varies considerably, from leaves of long, needle-like shape to broad flat leaves, or leaves divided like the fronds of small ferns.

Various species are widely dispersed in this State. In the Kimberley there is *D. physocarpa* with its remarkable bladder-like fruits. This is confined to basalt soils. Other species are found near watercourses, while the Goldfields and mulga country boast several very attractive forms, and there are, too, a number scattered throughout the South West, principally on granitic and lateritic soils, and these appear to favour elevations.

Of *Diplopeltis,* three species especially deserve mention. *D. huegelii* is a common, low shrub of the Darling Range, occurring in granite soils, usually among rocks, and flowering early in spring. It also occurs fairly frequently in the coastal limestones. In the Geraldton district is to be found a closely related species, *D. petiolaris*—perhaps only a broad-leaved form of *D. huegelii,*

◁ *Diplopeltis huegelii* Endl., a common low shrub of the Darling Range and coastal limestone districts.

RHAMNACEAE

Buckthorn family

NOT remarkable for the number of plants it contains or for extraordinary or showy flowers, the Buckthorn family is, nevertheless, an important one, almost cosmopolitan in distribution and comprising about 46 genera and 550 species. Closely related to the grape family *(Vitaceae)* the family can usually be recognised by its calyx-lobes usually larger than the petals and not overlapping in the bud but meeting at the edges only; its petals alternating with the calyx-lobes and usually smaller than them, and frequently hooded in the upper part and hiding the stamens which are placed in front of the petals.

Few of the *Rhamnaceae* are of economic importance, the best known probably being *Rhamnus purshiana* from North America which yields *cascara sagrada* from its bark but the common buckthorn, widely grown as a hedge plant, also provides a powerful cathartic and a yellow dye from its fruits. One local species *(Cryptandra leucophracta)* is a toxic plant, the active principle of which is not yet known.

△ *Dodonaea viscosa* Jacq.

while in the red sand of the desert grows the equally attractive *D. stuartii*.

The minga-bush of the mulga country *(Heterodendron oleifolium)* is a valued stock fodder but under certain conditions it may become toxic. It is a shrub or small tree with panicles of small yellowish-white flowers at the ends of the branches.

The whitewood of Kimberley and the De Grey and Fortescue districts *(Atalaya hemiglauca)* is an attractive small bushy tree with fruits that closely resemble those of the sycamore-maple of the northern hemisphere. The fruits of this species are poisonous to horses.

△ *Dodonaea boroniaefolia* G.Don.

Ten genera are recorded from Western Australia, four of which are tropical, the remainder being indigenous to the South West and southern interior. In the north is to be found *Alphitonia excelsa,* the red ash with a fine-grained timber of value to the cabinetmaker, common along the Glenelg and Prince Regent Rivers but scarce elsewhere. *Ventilago viminalis* is the supple-jack, a tree not unlike the peppermint of the South West but with small green flowers and ash-like winged fruits, a valuable browsing plant and highly regarded by pastoralists. *Enneaspermum cunninghamii,* known only from the stony, sandstone country around Admiralty Gulf, is a small tree with lustrous foliage and red fruits with red seeds. *Zizyphus* is a tree of the Ord River district.

In the South West there are six genera. Noteworthy among these is *Siegfriedia darwinioides,* a small shrub of the south coast near Ravensthorpe, rarely exceeding 600 mm in height with rolled leaves, dark green above but dull red with closely matted hairs underneath, and clusters of small flowers hidden among large, salmon-pink, fringed bracts. The remaining genera—*Pomaderris, Trymalium, Spyridium, Cryptandra* and *Blackallia*—are widely distributed and not particularly remarkable, although some species of *Trymalium,* with large panicles of small white flowers are reminiscent of some species of privet and could be a worthy addition to our gardens, while *Cryptandra grandiflora* of the Carnamah district is outstanding for its large heads of white flowers.

Cryptandra arbutiflora is found widely dispersed throughout the South West from the Dandaragan area to the south coast growing usually among granite rocks. Its creamy flowers bear a general resemblance to those of the Irish strawberry *(Arbutus unedo),* hence the specific epithet of *arbutiflora.* It is a shrub rarely exceeding a metre in height.

△ *Trymalium spathulatum* (Labill.) Ostf., a widely distributed member of the Buckthorn family.

△ *Rulingia densiflora* (Turcz.) Benth. . . . an erect, densely hairy shrub.

◁ *Spyridium globulosum* (Labill.) Benth. grows on the coast.

△ The Australian Hollyhock . . . *Lavatera plebeja* Sims.

BOMBACACEAE

Cotton family

MOST of the members of the Cotton family are to be found in tropical latitudes and, comprising about 33 genera of more or less 250 species, a number are of economic or horticultural importance—*Bombax,* native to tropical Asia, yields kapok; balsa wood is obtained from *Ochroma pyramidalis,* indigenous to tropical America; a species of *Gossypium* provides cotton, and *Hibiscus esculentus* provides okra, a common South American vegetable. Plants grown for ornament include many species of *Hibiscus, Gossypium,* and the pyramid tree *(Lagunaria patersonii),* so characteristic of the coastal gardens of Australia.

Western Australia has nine native genera: *Hibiscus, Brockmania, Thespesia, Alyogyne, Notoxylinon, Gossypium, Camptostemon, Adansonia* and *Bombax.*

Species of *Hibiscus* are widely distributed throughout the warmer parts of this State, being most common northwards from the De Grey River. Although the colours of the blossoms vary, violet and yellow predominate. In the South West there is the large flowered *H. wrayae,* frequently found from the Northampton district to the vicinity of the Phillips River, while on the Goldfields, eastwards from Merredin, the desert rose mallow *H. farragei* is common. It prefers clay soils, attains a height of two metres and its small pale violet or lilac blossoms, with hollyhock-like greyish-green foliage are to be seen from August to December.

Far away in the extreme north-west, in the vicinity of the Prince Regent, Glenelg and Calder Rivers grows the handsome *Thespesia macrophylla.* It is found on the banks of streams, attaining a height of 2.5 metres and flaunts its yellow, purple-centred flowers almost throughout the year.

Distant again—in the south—are the two species of *Alyogyne,* the "red-centred hibiscus" of the wheatlands and the Goldfields. These are to

◁ *Hibiscus farragei* F.Muell. . . . the desert rose mallow . . . common on the Goldfields, grows two metres high.

△ Variants of the Lilac Hibiscus *H.huegelii* Endl. are widely distributed in the southern part of Western Australia, from the Murchison River to the south coast east of Albany.

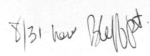

△ *Gossypium sturtianum* J.H. Willis, a West Australian species of cotton which grows in the dry interior.

be found in many situations and flower from November to March.

The white, usually purple or red-centred (but sometimes entirely rose-pink) flowers of *Notoxylinon* are to be seen only in tropical areas, being borne on small or trailing shrubs.

There are two species of cotton indigenous to Western Australia— *Gossypium sturtianum* of the dry interior and *G. robinsonii* confined to the areas between the De Grey and Cane Rivers of the North West.

The stems of *Camptostemon schultzii* are used by the aborgines of the Prince Regent River country for the manufacture of catamarans, the wood being extremely buoyant.

While popular interest may centre around such plants as cotton and balsa, this family also includes the extraordinary baobab trees, species of *Adansonia,* which are restricted to Africa, Madagascar, the Kimberley district of Western Australia and the Victoria River area of the Northern Territory. The local tree *(A. gregorii)* (almost identical in appearance with the common African *A. digitata)* is grotesque in appearance and, under our northern climatic conditions, rarely exceeds 10 metres in height, although it may attain a girth of over 18 metres. The result is a gouty trunk, often bottle-shaped and narrowed at the top whence the branches spread widely. It has large, bright green leaves and large scented white flowers in summer, but in winter the trees are normally leafless. Its pithy wood and cuticle-like bark enable this exotic-looking species to exist in defiance of the long dry cool season of the year. When decayed internally the bark callouses over the damaged surface and the hollowed trunk may serve as a rainwater tank.

A true kapok tree also exists in the wetter parts of Kimberley where the rich basaltic soils enables it to thrive. This is *Bombax malabaricum,* which produces most attractive large crimson flowers. It is not very common except to the north of the Prince Regent River.

△ *Hibiscus meraukensis* Hochr.

Alyogyne hakeifolia Giord. Alef . . . one of the "red-centred ▷ hibiscuses" of the wheatlands and Goldfields.

△ The West Australian baobab *Adansonia gregorii* F.Muell. may attain a girth of more than 18 metres, but rarely exceeds 10 metres in height. The trees shown are growing in the tropics north of Halls Creek.

B. sp. petals dead tree 9/2
Mullewa 9/2

STERCULIACEAE

Kurrajong family

△ *Brachychiton viscidulum* (W.V. Fitzg.) C.A. Gardn. . . . a tropical species of the Kurrajong family.

△ *Guichenotia macrantha* Turcz., the Large-Flowered Guichenotia, is found in the Geraldton district.

S OME of the tropical species of the kurrajongs are worthy of a place in tropical gardens, especially those with trusses of large scarlet flowers which are not uncommon in Kimberley and other parts of northern Australia.

In Western Australia there are eight genera comprising 18 species confined to the tropical north, while in the South-West there are eight genera of 76 species mostly confined to that area, although the common kurrajong (*Brachychiton gregorii*) occurs throughout the drier parts of the State.

In passing it should be noted that cocoa is derived from *Theobroma cacao* (a native of Central America), and cola is obtained from *Cola vera* and *C. acuminata* (natives of West Africa), and all three are members of the *Sterculiaceae*.

A characteristic of the family is the calyx, often large and coloured and much more attractive than the relatively small—sometimes absent—corolla of petals. The shrubs of the section within the family which exhibit this to a marked extent are very common in south-western Australia, and belong to the genera *Keraudrenia, Thomasia, Guichenotia, Lasiopetalum* and *Lysiosepalum*. These have much in common, differing mainly in the degree of division of the calyx and the veins of the same, and the commonest colours are violet, purple, red, pink and white.

The firebush (*Keraudrenia integrifolia*) is a shrub of about a metre in height which is common in gravelly soils or is sometimes associated with granite rocks. The calyx is purple-violet, sometimes blue, and when in blossom this plant is most attractive. Its common name arises from its appearance after a bush fire. The other species of this genus (*K. hermanniaefolia*) is found in the sandy tracts of the western coastal plain from Mogumber northwards to the Murchison River.

Among the more attractive members of the family is *Thomasia grandiflora* in which petals

◁ *Thomasia macrocarpa* Hueg. . . . the Large-Fruited Thomasia.

are totally absent, the flower having the general appearance of the flowers of some plants of the Potato family.

In other genera, locally common, the calyx is relatively smaller but the presence of sterile stamens, which assume the size and appearance of petals (and take a variety of forms), intermixed with true petals, impart to the flowers a curious appearance—not unlike small roses.

However, the large, petal-like calyx is seen to best advantage in the kurrajongs, which are species of *Brachychiton* and *Sterculia.* 9/2 *Muellera?*

The common kurrajong *(B. gregorii)* is a deciduous tree widely dispersed throughout the drier parts of the continent. The maple-like bright green leaves always provide refreshing contrast among the dull grey-green foliage of its associates. The leafless period is usually short and although the greenish-red flowers are not very attractive, the pyramidal habit of the tree has made it popular for parks and gardens.

In kurrajongs the flowers are usually unisexual and alike in appearance, with a large trumpet or bell-shaped calyx and no petals, and the stamens are united into a column, but the anthers throughout the family open in two distinct slits or pores.

Nearly all the tropical kurrajongs are deciduous and many bear their flowers in clusters on the old wood: the contrast of the black or dark grey trunk with the vivid scarlet of the large clusters of massive bell-shaped blossoms is most effective.

The seeds of the kurrajongs are produced in small, cup-shaped structures which consist of closely matted packing fibres in a curious, boat-shaped follicle or fruit. These seeds remain attached for a time but are shaken out of the fruit by the wind when maturity is attained.

VIOLACEAE
Violet family

THERE are no true violets (of the genus *Viola*) indigenous to Western Australia, the family being represented by the single genus *Hybanthus*. All the members of the family are herbs or, more rarely, shrubs, and about 400 species are arranged under some 16 genera which are found growing throughout the world, but are most common in the temperate regions.

The genus *Hybanthus* already referred to is divided into nine species, the commonest of which is that called the wild violet *(H. calycinus)* a common sub-shrub of the woodlands and forests of the South West, but most frequent in the limestone soils of the western coastal plain.

Other species, like *H. floribundus*, are shrubs growing to a height of a metre, and one—*H. epacroides*—found sparsely distributed over the eastern agricultural areas, is a small spiny shrub. All of the southern species have violet or bluish-white flowers.

In the tropical north there are two species; one has deep orange-red flowers *(H. aurantiacus)*, the other violet flowers *(H. enneaspermus)*.

The principal characteristics found in members of the family are the five free sepals, five petals—of which the lowest is the largest, the flowers being thus irregular in design; five stamens, and the ovary of one compartment with the ovules attached to the wall of the compartment—not to an axis. The presence of a spur to the corolla is often a distinguishing character in conjunction with the foregoing.

△ *Keraudrenia hermanniaefolia* J.Gray.

Wild violet . . . *Hybanthus calycinus* (Steud.) F.Muell. ▷

DILLENIACEAE

Hibbertia family

ELEVEN genera with 275 species comprise the *Dilleniacea*, and among the largest are *Dillenia* and *Hibbertia* which are found mainly in the tropical or warm temperate regions of the southern hemisphere.

The species of *Dillenia* are native to the Malay Peninsula and the adjacent islands, while the species of *Hibbertia* range from Malagasy eastwards to the Fiji Islands, but the far greater number are native to Australia, and in particular the South West. It is true that they are also found both in the tropical north and inland to the Macdonald Range, but nowhere are they such a feature of the landscape as they are in southwestern Australia from June to November where some 64 species enliven the countryside with their intense yellow flowers.

The two exceptions to this rule of yellow blossoms are *H. stellaris,* a dainty plant which often bears deep orange flowers, and *H. miniata* of the Darling Range which usually has orangered petals and violet-black anthers.

All of the species are shrubs or sub-shrubs and as much at home on the inland sandheaths as they are in the shady forest. The commonest of all is *H. hypericoides* which is a feature of the woodlands of the Perth district.

△ *Hibbertia cunninghamii* (Benth.) Steud. . . . 64 species of *Hibbertia* enliven the West Australian landscape.

Some of the *Hibbertias* are of lowly stature and creeping habit—for example, *H. lasiopus*—which has its large deep golden flowers on long stems. Some, like *H. perfoliata,* have the leaf attachment above the base so that the leaf appears to surround the stem. In a number the ornamental value of the flower is enhanced by the presence of chestnut-brown bracts surrounding the flower.

The genus is interesting botanically because of the diversity in arrangement of the stamens, and their union with or freedom from each other.

The solitary species of the genus *Pachynema* is found in the Northampton district. Its stems are leafless and rush-like.

Members of this family are most easily recognisable by the five free concave persistent sepals and the five, usually notched, deciduous petals which fall early; the usually numerous stamens which are variously arranged, and the almost free carpels, commonly two to five in number, which open outwards to liberate the seeds.

◁ *Hibbertia lasiopus* Benth. . . . as much at home on the inland sandheath as in the shady forest.

△ *Hibbertia hypericoides* (D.C.) Benth. . . . the most common species and a feature of Perth woodlands.

△ ▽ *Hibbertia miniata* C.A. Gardn. . . . one of two *Hibbertia* exceptions which do not have yellow blossoms.

△ *Hibbertia cuneiformis* (Labill.) Gilq.

△ *Hibbertia miniata* C.A. Gardn.

Hibbertia lasiopus Benth. ▷

THYMELAEACEAE

Daphne family

△ *Pimelea spectabilis* (Fisch. et Mey.) Lindl.

The Qualup-bell . . . *Pimelea physodes* Hook. ▷

FROM the familiar scented daphnes of our gardens it is a far cry to the Qualup-bell and few observers would find much in common in these, yet both belong to the same family. Two genera of the *Thymelaeaceae* are found in Western Australia, and both carry tubular four-lobed flowers; *Pimelea* possessing only two stamens, while the one other genus found in this State is the extremely rare *Wikstroemia* of the north-west Kimberley, which has eight stamens.

There are 40 species of *Pimelea* native to Western Australia, of which four species—confined to Kimberley—have the four bracts united into a cup from which the brilliant blood-red flowers protrude.

It is, in fact, the arrangement of the flowers of *Pimelea* which is the principal characteristic of the greater number of its species. With the exception of a few shrubs (mainly to be found in the arid regions) the blossoms are massed in heads surrounded by an envelope of over-lapping petal-like bracts. When these exceed the length of the flowers, and the head is drooping, we find those species which resemble the Qualup-bell *(P. physodes):* the true flowers are to be found crowded within the bell-shaped involucre. Similarly, when the bracts are not longer than the flowers—as in *P. spectabilis,* and again in *P. suaveolens,* in which the bracts are still shorter, the flowers protrude.

Among local species, *P. clavata* is found in the karri forests and the bracts are minute; the flowers are yellowish-white in small clusters at the ends of the branches. *P. spectabilis* is not uncom-

△ *Pimelea sulphurea* Meisn. . . . another of the 40 species of *Pimelea* native to Western Australia.

mon in the Darling Range to the east of Perth and flowers in September, while *P. suaveolens* in a number of forms is widely dispersed, the largest-flowered forms being found in the Darling Range and with these the bracts turn from green to lemon-yellow.

The Qualup-bell *(P. physodes)* is so-called from its common occurrence at Qualup on the Gairdner River, whence it extends to the vicinity of Ravensthorpe on the Phillips River. The large bracts of the flowers are variously coloured, ranging from purple to apple-green or yellow.

In some species, however, bracts are not present and, for identification, reliance must be placed on the number of parts of the flower and the one-chambered ovary in the base of the flower, with its solitary pendulous ovule which ripens with the seed.

Pimelea ferruginea Labill. ▷

△ Karri (*Eucalyptus diversicolor* F.Muell.) forest in Warren National Park, near Pemberton.

△ The Myrtle family, one of the most important plant families of Australia, embraces both trees, *Eucalyptus,* and attractive under-shrub *Kunzea baxteri* (Klotzach) Schau. shown in this glimpse of Kings Park, Perth.

MYRTACEAE

Myrtle family

THE Myrtle family provides in the landscape of Western Australia the tallest trees and some of the most attractive under-shrubs for it is one of the largest and most important families of plants in this continent.

It comprises some 80 genera and more than 3,000 species of which 33 genera and some 325 species are native to this State, being widely distributed over the whole area. Particularly rich in its representation in the South West—to which the greater number are restricted—it is also equally at home in the tropical north and in the dry red sand of the interior. All members of the family to a greater or lesser extent contain oil in the foliage.

Its economic importance to Western Australia is outstanding for it provides most of the hardwood timbers as well as useful tanning materials from the bark and wood of several species (especially wandoo timber and mallet bark); it includes a number of species yielding valuable essential oils from their foliage and sometimes from the flower buds; it is important to bee-keepers because of the nectar and pollen yielded by its blossoms.

△ White . . . *Verticordia helmsii* S.Moore.

MYRTLE FAMILY

Apart from all of that, some of the species are so floriferous that they rank among the most handsome plants in the world. The prevailing colours of the blossoms range from white through the various shades of pink to crimson but departures from this range are found in the intense orange hues seen in some *Verticordias* and *Eremaeas,* and in the deep violet of *Calytrix, Wehlia, Eremaea* and *Lhotzkya.* Blue flowers do not occur.

△ Pink . . . *Beaufortia schaueri* Preiss.

Badgingara

9/3

△ Orange . . . *Eremaea beaufortioides* Benth.

△ Violet . . . *Calytrix strigosa* A.Cunn.

◁ Crimson . . . *Beaufortia squarrosa* Schau.

The *Myrtaceae* can be conviently divided into two groups—that is to say, if one ignores those *Myrtaceae* of the tropics which carry berries.

In the first of these called *Leptospermeae,* are the two largest genera, *Eucalyptus* and *Melaleuca* (tea-trees). *Eucalyptus* is characterised by the total absence of any free petals to its flowers, for such are fused to form a bud cap (operculum) which is pushed off the calyx by the expanding stamens (see illustration of *Eucalyptus macro-carpa* opposite). *Melaleuca,* however, possesses petals and the stamens (united into bundles) form an attractive feature of the flower. All species in this group have woody fruits which liberate their seeds when ripe.

The second group, largely Western Australian, is called the *Chamelaucieae.* The seeds of such plants are not liberated from the fruit when it is ripe—in fact there is no fruit development at all, the slightly enlarged and withered flower containing one seed. It is these plants which are usually difficult to germinate from seed, for such are usually planted in the soil. Under natural conditions they germinate on the surface of the soil among the plant debris which surrounds them. (An examination of *Verticordia* "fruit," with its feathery calyx, will readily show why, in nature, the seeds could not be buried.)

In addition to *Eucalyptus,* comprising nearly 150 species from giant karri to dwarf mallee

△ *Eucalyptus macrocarpa* Hook . . . the petals are fused to form a
▽ bud cap which is pushed off the calyx by the expanding stamens.

△ *Melaleuca steedmanii* C.A. Gardn. . . . the stamens, united into bundles, are an attractive feature of the flower.

shrubs, and *Melaleuca,* from the giant cajuput of the north to the lowly sand heath plants of the South West, other attractive genera in the first group mentioned and in which the stamens are an attractive feature (being much longer than the petals) are *Beaufortia, Calothamnus, Conothamnus, Lamarchea* (in which the stamens are united in the lower part to form a complete tube) *Phymatocarpus* and *Eremaea.* Differences in the anther-structure serve to separate the genera.

Other examples of these woody-fruited plants which shed their seeds (but in these cases the petals are as prominent as the stamens) are found in the genera *Agonis, Leptospermum, Kunzea, Hypocalymma, Baeckea* and *Scholtzia,* all of which have free stamens; *Callistemon,* in which the stamens are very much longer than the inconspicuous petals; *Astartea,* in which the petals are the attractive part of the flower, the stamens not being free but arranged in five small bundles; and *Balaustion,* with orange or scarlet flowers (much resembling those of the pomegranate), which genus has but two species and both of these are small shrubs.

In the second group, the *Chamelaucieae,* are included 13 genera, the greater number of which are indigenous to Western Australia and all almost certainly had their origin here. Six of these are entirely restricted to the South West. Of all of them the most notable are *Actinodium, Verticordia, Darwinia, Chamelaucium, Pileanthus, Thryptomene* and *Micromyrtus.*

Having indicated very broadly how the family is divided, a few of the individual species merit more detailed description.

△ *Calothamnus sanguineus* Labill. . . . the stamens, much longer than the petals, are an attractive feature.

△ *Callistemon phoeniceus* Lindl. . . . stamens very much longer than the inconspicuous petals.

86   A much-enlarged view of *Hypocalymma robustum* Endl. ▷ to show the free stamens and equally prominent petals.

△ *Eucalyptus macrocarpa* Hook., commonly called mottlecah, has the largest flowers of all eucalypts. *Dandaragan*

The largest flowered species of *Eucalyptus* is that commonly called mottlecah *(E. macrocarpa)*, a shrub two to 5.5 metres in height, usually a straggling growth. In the typical form the flowers are large and stalkless, the leaves vary in shape and are usually stalkless and there is variation in the shape of the bud-cap and in the colour of the filaments—from deep crimson to rose-pink or yellowish-white. The largest flowers measure nearly 75 mm across. To be found from near Mingenew to Bruce Rock, it is, however, most common in the region of the Hill and Moore Rivers and near Tammin. In the form sometimes known as *E. rhodantha* the flowers are stalked, and this form is found between the Hill River and New Norcia. The shrubs grow in white sand and flower from November to March, although the flowers may be seen almost throughout the year.

Eucalyptus rhodantha Blakeley & Steedman grows between ▷ the Hill River and New Norcia.

MYRTLE FAMILY

Inhabiting sandy soil among rocks near the south coast, *E. preissiana* is a shrub which, rarely exceeding a metre in height, has a widely branched habit. The bell-shaped, rather large fruits are very decorative. A larger species is *E. pyriformis,* a shrub usually of untidy growth which may reach a height of 4.5 metres or so. The relative length of the calyx-tubes and the stalks give these plants considerable variation in characteristics. The long-stalked forms are found towards the west of this species' range —Coorow to Goomalling, while the short-stalked and more robust fruited forms are found far inland, mainly in the Eastern Goldfields. *E. kingsmillii* is a very closely related species, with the buds, and similarly the fruits, longitudinally eight-ribbed, and the colour of the filaments varies from rose-pink to white. This latter species inhabits the sandy country and has a prolonged flowering season from September to February.

△ Large-fruited mallee *Eucalyptus pyriformis* Turcz.

▽ Wattle and coral vine *Kennedia coccinea* Vent. in jarrah *(Eucalyptus marginata* Donn. ex Sm.) forest near Augusta.

△ Red-flowering gum *Eucalyptus ficifolia* F. Muell. in Kings Park.

△ Gungurru . . . *Eucalyptus caesia* Benth.

△ Illyarrie . . . *Eucalyptus erythrocorys* F. Muell.

△ The red-flowering gum *Eucalyptus ficifolia* F. Muell., found near the Bow River, is now widely cultivated.

△ Fuchsia mallee *Eucalyptus forrestiana* Diels.
▽ *Eucalyptus lehmannii* (Schau.) Benth. . . . finger-like bud caps, green flowers, seed capsules fused to form the fruit.

▽ Swamp yate *Eucalyptus occidentalis* Endl.

△ The square-fruited mallee *Eucalyptus tetraptera* Turcz.

▽ Bell-fruited mallee *Eucalyptus preissiana* Schau.

△ Tuarts *Eucalyptus gomphocephala* D.C. near Busselton. This is the only natural tuart forest in the world and the only savannah forest in the State. The tuarts grow to 36 metres, occur in a narrow coastal belt.

△ Paper-barks *Melaleuca cuticularis* Labill. in the Albany district.

▽ Wind-bent river gum *Eucalyptus camaldulensis* Dehn. on the Greenough plains.

△ *Melaleuca glaberrima* F. Muell.

△ *Melaleuca conothamnoides* C.A. Gardn. . . . grows in the gravel and sand north from Pithara to Mullewa.

△ *Melaleuca macronychia* Turcz.

Melaleuca macronychia is one of the bottle-brush tea-trees, and occurs as a shrub two to 2.5 metres high in the vicinity of granite rocks in watercourses between Tammin and Bruce Rock, flowering in December. *M. trichophylla* is a shrub normally less than 600 mm high, common in gravelly or sandy-gravelly soils over a wide area of the South West, and it flowers in September and October. Another species, *M. conothamnoides* is an attractive inhabitant of the gravelly-sandy soils northwards from Pithara to Mullewa, flowering from July to February.

△ The claw flower *Melaleuca pulchella* R.Br.

93

△ *Melaleuca nematophylla* F.Muell.

△ Rough honey-myrtle *Melaleuca scabra* R.Br.

△ *Melaleuca leptospermoides* Schau.

△ Robin red-breast bush *Melaleuca lateritia* Otto.

◁ Chenille honey-myrtle *Melaleuca huegelii* Endl.

MYRTLE FAMILY

The genus *Beaufortia* is confined to Western Australia and comprises 16 species. Three of these are plants which carry large spikes of flowers and are found near the south coast. *B. sparsa* is the vermilion-flowered swamp bottle-brush of the Albany-Denmark district. Other species have smaller flower spikes and yet others are smaller still. *B. squarrosa* is perhaps the most widespread extending between the Murchison and Canning Rivers; it has two forms—that on P. 84, an erect, fairly densely foliaged shrub of the Wongan Hills district, and the other, a low, straggling shrub exhibiting staminal bundles ranging from an intense crimson to orange and pale yellow. *B. schaueri* is a small shrub rarely exceeding three feet in height; it extends from the hills of the Stirling Range eastwards to the Phillips River and flowers for the greater part of the year.

Some of the 24 species of *Calothamnus*, frequently known as one-sided bottle-brushes, are noteworthy for the richness of their flower colouring. All are restricted to Western Australia and the best is undoubtedly *C. homalophyllus,* but *C. sanguineus* is one of the most widespread, favouring granite soils and *C. quadrifidus* is also a common species. It is usually found in clay or gravelly-clay soils throughout the South West where it attains a height of three metres or more, flowering during the latter half of the year. *C. microcarpus* is found in sand or clay heath country in the southern districts, especially around the Stirling Range.

△ *Beaufortia purpurea* Lindl.

△ *Calothamnus homalophyllus* F.Muell.

▽ One-sided bottlebrush *Calothamnus quadrifidus* R.Br.

▽ *Calothamnus blepharospermus* F.Muell.

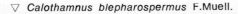

△ Swamp tea-tree *Leptospermum ellipticum* Endl. . . . in flower during most of the year.

Another common shrub of the low-lying places near the coast in the South West is *Leptospermum ellipticum*. It favours soils subject to inundation in the winter and the flowers, ranging from white to a pale rose-pink, may be seen almost throughout the year.

The genus *Kunzea* consists of 11 species which exhibit considerable variation. *K. baxteri* from the Cape Arid district might be mistaken for a *Melaleuca;* others have smaller flowers in which the stamens are less conspicuous. *K. pulchella* must be regarded as one of our most curious plants for it grows not in soil but in the crevices of bald granite rocks and resembles the dwarf Japanese conifers but is of more irregular habit. White flowered forms also occur. This species extends from the vicinity of Lake Moore to the south coast near Esperance and blossoms in October and November. *K. recurva* is a common shrub of sandy, low-lying spots through the lower South West, while *K. preissiana* inhabits depressions in the poor sandy tracts of the southern littoral, and this also flowers in October and November.

▽ *Leptospermum sericeum* Labill.

△ *Kunzea pulchella* (Lindl.) A.S. George . . . in rock crevices.

▽ *Kunzea jucunda* Diels.

△ A shrub found throughout the lower South West, *Kunzea recurva var. montana* Schau., and beetle, highly magnified.

▽ *Kunzea baxteri (Klotzsch)* Schau., from the Cape Arid district, has many features in common with *Melaleuca.*

△ Swan River myrtle *Hypocalymma robustum* Endl.

The 13 species of *Hypocalymma* are confined to the South West and the best known of these is the Swan River myrtle (*H. robustum*). Its pink flowers are common on the western coastal plain and in the Darling Range, where it begins to flower in the winter. In the southern forests, where it is cooler and damper, *H. robustum* may still be found in bloom as late as January. Other species have white, yellow or deep red flowers. Among these is *H. speciosum,* found in the Stirling Range, a shrub rarely exceeding 300 mm in height. It occurs in peaty soils among rocks and flowers in October.

△ Albany bottle-brush *Callistemon speciosus* (Sims) D.C.

△ Camphor myrtle *Baeckea camphorosmae* Endl.

△ *Hypocalymma speciosum* Turcz.

Sometimes known as the eczema-bush—because an infusion of the leaves is said to relieve skin diseases—*Baeckea camphorosmae* favours clay soils and is found in the Darling Range near Perth and also near Collie. It flowers in summer.

The Albany bottle-brush *(Callistemon speciosus),* is the largest-flowered species of the genus, the axis growing out into a leafy branch before the buds have matured. Growing in sandy, swampy places along the south coast, it is most abundant near King George Sound but extends, in swampy places, almost as far northwards as Perth. *C. phoeniceus* is the other local representative of the genus. It may be found from the north-west of this State southwards to the Hotham and Murray Rivers. In the northern parts of its range it occurs as a tree up to six metres tall, but in the south it is found as a shrub rarely exceeding 2.5 metres in height. It is commonly grown in cultivation but in natural conditions it flourishes along watercourses, especially where water lies close to the surface in winter, yet it is equally at home in sand or clay.

Wilroy 9/2

△ *Balaustion microphyllum* C.A.Gardn.

△ Scarlet feather flower *Verticordia grandis* J.Drumm.
. . . most handsome and most popular *Verticordia*.

The two species of the genus *Balaustion* are confined to the South West, *B. pulcherrimum* is a prostrate shrub found southwards from Perenjori to Kellerberrin and eastwards to Southern Cross. Lying close to the ground, the plant radiates to form a clump a metre in diameter and it seldom exceeds 100 mm in height. More erect is *B. microphyllum,* restricted to the country around Pindar and Wilroy. Its flowers have their calyces covered with transparent papillae of a pale green. Both species flower in September and October.

The solitary species of *Actinodium (A. cunninghamii),* is the swamp daisy of the south coastal areas. Its complicated inflorescence consists of an inner "head" of red, small and fertile flowers. The outer ring of white sterile ray flowers is arranged much like the bracts or female flowers of the familiar daisy-type of blossom. This structure is so peculiar within the Myrtle family that it can confuse a botanist.

△ Swamp daisy *Actinodium cunninghamii* Schau. ex Lindl.

△ *Verticordia chrysantha* Endl. in the Geraldton district.

The species of *Verticordia* are called feather-flowers and are almost entirely Western Australian. The common name arises from a characteristic of the plants in that the calyx-lobes are deeply divided into feather-like divisions. The calyx-lobes are usually five in number but some have auxiliary divisions, and some few have, in addition, other appendages which make the calyx structure very complex. The tropical *V. cunninghamii* attains the proportions of a small tree, but all other species are small shrubs. In all, 48 species are known and of these possibly *V. grandis* is the most handsome and most popular. It is found on the open sand heath country between the Moore and Murchison rivers and, alone of this genus, carries at least some flowers throughout the year. It inhabits poor sand and, but for the difficulty of transplanting it (by reason of its wide, deep root system) and of growing it from seed (because of the low viability of its seeds), it seems certain it would be commonly cultivated. *V. muelleriana* is one of the tallest shrub species, its erect, slender, twiggy stems sometimes reaching two metres. Also common between the Moore and Murchison rivers, this species extends eastwards beyond Morawa, and flowers late in the spring and through the summer. *V. picta* is a small shrub common over a wide area of the sand heath country and blooms from September until late in November. Other species of the genus have white or lilac flowers *(V. oculata),* or yellow, white or orange *(V. nitens),* the last-named showing its richly coloured blossoms at the close of the year.

Verticordia chrysantha Endl. close-up ▷

△ *Verticordia picta* Endl. . . . a small shrub which
grows widely in the sand heath country.

△ *Verticordia lindleyi* Schau.

△ *Verticordia mitchelliana* C.A.Gardn.

△ *Verticordia nitens* (Lindl.) Schau.
. . . Morrison feather flower.

△ *Verticordia muelleriana* E. Pritzel . . .
sometimes nearly two metres tall.

△ The beautiful pink woolly feather flower *Verticordia monadelpha* Turcz.

▽ *Verticordia ovalifolia* Meisn.

▽ *Verticordia etheliana* C.A.Gardn.

MYRTLE FAMILY

Twenty-nine species of *Darwinia* are found in this State, and these fall into two groups: those with large, coloured, petal-like bracts and those with small bracts—or at least bracts which do not much exceed the flowers. In the first group are eight species, mainly inhabiting the hills of the South West. *D. meeboldii* is the largest of these, attaining a height of two metres, with a few erect straight branches and growing in stony, peaty soil not far from Cranbrook, where it flowers in October. *D. macrostegia* is confined to stony patches of peaty soil on the peaks of the Stirling Range. Its tulip-like heads are as much as 60 mm in length and it flowers in September and October. *D. leiostyla,* also found in the Stirling Range and at Middle Mount Barren, favours similar situations and flowers at about the same time. Other mountain bells are *D. hypericifolia* of the Stirling Range, *D. squarrosa* of the same district, *D. carnea* of the hills of the Moore River district, *D. pimelioides* of the Darling Range, and the beautiful lemon-yellow-bracted *D. collina* from the highest summits of the Stirling Range. In the second group—with the smaller bracts—is *D. vestita* a straight stemmed shrub, rarely more than 300 mm in height, with white or deep red (rarely pink) flowers. It is common in the vicinity of Albany and the Stirling Range, but is found as far to the west as the Vasse district and eastwards to Esperance. It flowers in the spring.

△ *Darwinia leiostyla* (Turcz.) Domin. . . . high on the Stirling Range.

104

Darwinia squarrosa (Turcz.) Domin. . . . another of ▷ the mountain bells found in the same district.

△ The yellow mountain bell *Darwinia collina* (Turcz.) Domin. grows only on Bluff Knoll, highest peak in the Stirlings.

▽ *Darwinia oldfieldii* Benth.

△ *Darwinia squarrosa* from another angle.

▽ Lemon-scented myrtle *Darwinia citriodora* (Endl.) Benth.

8/3. Coorow - varias colon

△ Geraldton wax-flower *Chamelaucium uncinatum* Schau.

The 12 species of *Chamelaucium* are closely related to *Darwinia* but the flowers of the former are never in close heads, their structure being typified in the common Geraldton wax-flower *(C. uncinatum)*. This species, however, is somewhat misnamed because it extends well over 500 km along the coastal limestone country from the Murchison River to the vicinity of Perth. In the wild state the plants are of two types—one with white and the other with deep rose flowers. This shrub varies from one to five metres in height; it prefers a red sand and flowers from August to November. *C. megalopetalum* is much more attractive. It is a bushy, widely branched shrub and rarely exceeds 600 mm in height. Its flowers are larger than those of *C. uncinatum* and, at first white, they turn pink and finally red or purple (like those of *Hibiscus mutabilis)*. It is found from Southern Cross to the south coast, flowering from August to December on open sand heaths.

Pileanthus ranks high among the ornamental shrubs of Western Australia and its three species are all restricted to this State. A characteristic of the genus is that it develops ten calyx-lobes—while other plants have four or five. The white-flowered *P. limacis* is found on the north-west coast above Shark Bay. *P. filifolius,* the largest-flowered species, is a shrub a metre tall with slender erect stems and leaves not unlike those of the Geraldton wax-flower. The buds are enclosed between two lemon-yellow bracts and the petals range from an intense pink to a geranium lake. It is one of the most striking plants of the flora of Western Australia and it is astonishing to find that it is not in cultivation. Coming into

△ *Chamelaucium drummondii* Meisn.

△ *Pileanthus filifolius* Meisn. . . . one of the most striking flowers of Western Australia.

◁ The Cranbrook bell *Darwinia meeboldii* C.A.Gardn.

△ *Pileanthus peduncularis* Endl. . . . commonly called copper-cups.

blossom in November and remaining so until January, it is strange that petals of such delicacy can endure the heat of the summer months, the plants growing in sand on open sand heaths. The range of the species is from the Murchison River southwards to the Moore River. *P. peduncularis,* commonly known as copper-cups, has a much more extensive range, being found from the Murchison River southwards to Moora and eastwards to Merredin. It is not more than 450 mm in height, has shorter leaves than *P. filifolius,* flowers from August to December and the best forms are found near the Murchison River.

A number of extremely floriferous species, with masses of blossoms hiding the foliage, are included in the genus *Calytrix,* which comprises 30 species in all. The colours range from white to deep amethystine violet, with red, pink and yellow species as well. These are all plants of the sand heaths, or of gravelly or granite soils. The genus can be recognised by its calyx-lobes which terminate in bristle-like points, and the calyx-tube is spindle-shaped. Because of the densely flowered nature of some of the violet-blossomed species, the plants are sometimes referred to as heather, but there is no relationship between them.

Related to *Calytrix* are the genera *Lhotzkya* and *Wehlia,* the latter including a number of species bearing flowers of a rich purple colour, although another is pink and one yellow. The calyx-lobes and petals are not very dissimilar from *Calytrix* but are not bristle-pointed.

Wehlia thryptomenoides F.Muell. ▷

△ *Lhotzkya brevifolia* Schau.

△ *Calytrix angulata* Lindl.

△ *Calytrix brachyphylla* Turcz. . . . . calyx-lobes terminating in bristle-like points distinguish this genus.

△ *Calytrix variabilis* Lindl.

△ *Calytrix tenuifolia* Meisn.

△ *Thryptomene denticulata* (F.Muell.) Benth.

The two remaining genera of the *Chamelaucium* group are *Micromyrtus* and *Thryptomene,* shrubs ranging from those of dwarf stature to plants up to three metres tall. The flowers are much like those of *Baeckea* in appearance but the ovary is one-chambered, in common with the remainder of this group.

As to family characteristics—the plants are all woody trees or shrubs, with oil dots on the foliage; the petals, except in Eucalyptus, are all distinct and free from one another, and when the flower is in bud these overlap. The calyx-lobes, petals and stamens are all placed on the top of the ovary, which is united to the calyx-tube, and the style is not divided or branched. The ovules and seeds are attached to the axis of those fruits which are more than one-chambered, and usually numerous; in the one-chambered fruits (consisting of the enlarged and withered flower) the ovules are attached at or near the base, or pendulous from the apex, or arise from a thread-like placenta which extends from the base to the apex of the cavity.

HALORAGACEAE

Water-milfoil family

WHILE the Australian representatives of the Water-milfoil family are noteworthy because of their small, often minute, leaves, it is curious that the prickly rhubarb (of the genus *Gunnera* of this family), found in South America but not in Australia, has leaves which are over 1.8 metres in diameter, making these the largest-leaved plants in the world.

The family comprises eight genera and about 100 species, widely dispersed, but never taking a prominent place in the landscape.

In Western Australia we have four genera, two of which—*Myriophyllum,* the water-milfoil from which the family takes its name, and *Meziella,* are found in wet situations or even growing submerged in water, and much resembling horse-tail plants. Of the remaining two genera, *Haloragis* offers only one really attractive species and this is to be found on the south coast. The genus *Glischrocaryon,* however, consists of three local species, all of which are attractive by reason of their bright sulphur-yellow or lemon-yellow blossoms and their hop-like fruits.

G. aureum is the commonest of the species. It attains a height of over a metre, has pithy

△ *Glischrocaryon aureum* (Lindl.) Orchard. . . . bright yellow blossoms, hop-like fruits.

stems, small narrow leaves and wide corymbs of densely crowded blossoms. It is equally at home in sandy depressions or on high sandy or gravelly heath, where it flowers in the spring and early summer. Its range extends from the Murchison River southwards to the Vasse district and eastwards to Coolgardie.

Another, but similar species, *G. roei*, is more selective in the country it inhabits, growing only in sand on open heaths or in sandy-gravelly soil in open formations. Smaller in habit, and with smaller inflorescences, its fruits are more inflated and in colour range from yellow to brick-red. This species extends from the Murchison River to the eastern agricultural districts and the Goldfields.

The characteristics of the family include the insertion of the small calyx-lobes, and petals (when present) above the ovary, which has two, three or four chambers and a corresponding number of styles, with the pendulous seeds solitary in each compartment.

It thus has a close affinity to the Carrot family, from which it is best separated by the fact that in the Carrot family the flowers are differently arranged, being always in umbels or heads, whereas in the Water-milfoil family the flowers are either solitary or arranged otherwise.

UMBELLIFERAE

Carrot family

SOCRATES, it may be remembered, was given an infusion of the poisonous hemlock to drink after he had been condemned to death, and this plant—with the carrot, parsnip, celery, fennel, angelica, parsley, caraway, coriander and dill—is a member of the *Umbelliferae*. Widely dispersed in Western Australia are 13 native genera and 71 species, although this is but a small part of the Carrot family, which, totalling 126 genera and about 2,950 species, is cosmopolitan in distribution yet is generally found in the temperate regions of the northern hemisphere.

Few species are of horticultural value, and the three Western Australian plants important in this respect are the blue lace flower (*Trachymene caerulea*), the Southern Cross (*Xanthosia rotundifolia*), and the flannel flowers (species of *Actinotus*), the last named having the appearance of daisies in which the ray-florets are woolly-plumed. The sea holly (*Eryngium*) is often cultivated and belongs to this family.

Some genera favour wet situations, such as *Hydrocotyle, Neosciadium, Homalosciadium* and *Centella;* others are found in dry places, sometimes in shade, but sometimes—as with *Chlaenosciadium*—in the bare sandy spots of the open plains of the Eastern Goldfields.

The blue lace flower (*Trachymene caerulea*) is an herbaceous species found in the coastal limestone areas between the Moore and Serpentine rivers. It attains a height of about 450 mm with

△ *Eryngium pinnatifidum* Bunge . . . spike-like flower heads, whitish when young, becoming blue or purple.

The blue lace flower *Trachymene caerulea* Grah. ▷

grey, finely divided, hairy leaves, and umbels on long stems. The flowers are sometimes suffused with pink. The remaining species of this genus are not noteworthy; most are found in the sandy woods of the country of the western plain between the Swan and Vasse rivers. Two shrubby species of *Trachymene* have large swollen roots which are very aromatic and were formerly used by the aboriginal population—though for what purpose remains unknown.

The genus *Xanthosia* with 12 species contains some very attractive plants, one being the Southern Cross *(X. rotundifolia),* so named because of the four-rayed compound umbels in which the small umbels (partial umbels) are arranged in a cruciform pattern. This is found close to the south coast, is common between Mount Barker and King George Sound, and attains a height of a metre, favouring shady places.

The species of the flannel flowers are handsome herbaceous plants, one of which, *Actinotus*

△ Southern Cross *Xanthosia rotundifolia* D.C. . . . . common on the south coast between Mt. Barker and King George Sound.

superbus only occurs after bushfires, and then for only two or three years or possibly not to recur at all. It is found in tea-tree country in the eastern agricultural areas. *A. leucocephalus* is a larger plant growing in the Darling Range among granite rocks. It possesses less massive flowers.

The plants of this family, which is a natural one, can be readily recognised by the arrangement of the flowers, each flower being borne on a stalk, a number of which arise from the one point and radiate like the ribs of an umbrella. Sometimes the flowers are arranged in a simple umbrella-like arrangement (a simple umbel); at other times the umbel becomes complex, and consists of a number of umbels, the common stalk of each being in turn arranged in an umbel, so that the whole resembles a number of umbrellas arranged at the tips of a main umbrella. In a few examples (especially in *Eryngium)* the flowers are condensed into a spike, or what at first sight appears to be a spike.

△ *Xanthosia tomentosa* A.S.George.

EPACRIDACEAE

Heath family

TWO families bear the common name of heath: the *Ericaceae* or true heath family, found extensively in South Africa, Europe and the mountainous regions of the old and new world, and the southern heaths, *Epacridaceae*, a smaller family of 23 genera and about 350 species restricted to non-tropical Australia, New Zealand, several Pacific islands and Patagonia.

The *Epacridaceae* are well represented in southwestern Australia and do not extend into the dry interior. There are 15 native genera and 172 species, of which most belong to the genus *Leucopogon* (with 98 species). Other genera worth noting are *Andersonia, Cosmelia, Sphenotoma, Lysinema, Styphelia, Astroloma, Brachyloma, Conostephium, Needhamia, Oligarrhena* and *Coleanthera*.

The many species of *Leucopogon* do not exhibit much variation in their form or in their flowers which, with two exceptions, are white. One, the tassel-shrub *(L. verticillata)* is remarkable for its whorled leaves which are up to 150 mm in length and are of very attractive colouring when young.

Again with two exceptions, the species of *Andersonia* are small shrubs with flowers which consist, in the main, of a purple-pink calyx and blue corolla. These are seen to advantage in the opossums'-tails *(A. caerulea)* of the heaths around King George Sound. Other examples of this colouring are to be seen in a number of species of which perhaps the most common is *A. sprengelioides,* frequently found in the granite soils of the Darling Range. Two large species are found only on the highest summits of the Stirling Range: *A. axilliflora* has large leaves, 40 mm or more in length, while *A. echinocephala* has smaller leaves, but both are shrubs up to three metres in height.

△ Tassel shrub *Leucopogon verticillata* R.Br.

▽ *Andersonia echinocephala* (Stschegl.) Druce . . . only in Stirlings.

▽ *Andersonia sprengelioides* R.Br. . . . frequently found in the granite soils of the Darling Range.

△ On the summit of Bluff Knoll, highest peak of the Stirling Range . . . *Andersonia echinocephala* (Stschegl.) Druce is the **spiny** shrub; *Acacia drummondii* Lindl. the wattle, and the shrub with serrated leaves *Dryandra concinna* R.Br.

▽ *Sphenotoma dracophylloides* Sond. . . . a lovely species found in the southern districts.

HEATH FAMILY

A few species have crimson flowers.

Of a genus notable for the rich red of its comparatively large flowers is *Cosmelia rubra* which occurs in bogs around King George Sound. The species of *Sphenatoma* are all found in southern districts. In Western Australia they are confined to the boggy places along the south coast or in peaty, stony soil in the Stirling and Porongorup ranges. A fine example is *S. dracophylloides,* the lovely flowers of which are of considerable decorative value.

The four species of *Lysinema* are characterised by the long tubular flowers, usually yellowish-white or creamy, and the brown, overlapping bracts at the base; the common name of curry-and-rice possibly arises because of this contrast of brown and yellowish-white. *Styphelia* has both red and white flowers, and of the five species *S. tenuiflora* is the most common. This is a shrub with bright green leaves and very slender yellowish-white flowers which come into their fulness at the commencement of winter—almost, if not quite, the first flowers of the season.

Astroloma is perhaps the most attractive genus of all the southern heaths. These are all small shrubs with Erica-like blossoms, the colours being red, pink, white and one (*A. ciliatum*) is both purple and green. *A. microcalyx* is found in the vicinity of the Swan River and has somewhat

△ *Sphenotoma dracophylloides* Sond. . . . in the Stirling Range.

inflated flowers, but *A. xerophyllum* is probably the most common, being found everywhere in the sandy woods which extend between the Murchison and Murray rivers.

Of the two species of *Brachyloma, B. preissii* is common in shady, tree-covered areas around Perth; it has deep green leaves and small but rich rose-pink or red flowers. *Conostephium* is characterised by its purple-pointed corolla with very small lobes exceeding the white sepals. *C. pendulum,* sometimes called the pearl-flower, is common in sand anywhere on the coastal plain and has an extended flowering season. It is the most frequently found of the five species of this genus, which is restricted to south-western Australia.

The remaining six genera are not common, and some have a very restricted range. The small *Needhamia pumilio* and the also dwarfed *Oligarrhena,* which are both confined to the south coastal districts, are perhaps the most familiar, and the most remarkable of all are the three species of *Coleanthera,* with red flowers, the lobes of the corolla becoming rolled and exposing the anthers, which form a conspicuous cone round the style. This rare genus is also confined to the sandy heaths of the south coast.

◁ The pearl flower *Conostephium pendulum* Benth.

Badgingarra 9/3

115

△ Red swamp Astroloma . . . *Astroloma stomarrhena* Sond.

△ *Styphelia tenuiflora* Lindl. . . . first flowers of the season.

▽ Moss-leaved heath *Astroloma ciliatum* (Lindl.) Druce.

GENTIANACEAE

Gentian family

MANY of the Gentians are valued plants of rock and alpine gardens, notable for the richness of their blue flowers. In all, 70 genera belong to this family and consist of about 800 species, of which five genera are found in Western Australia.

The genera native to this State are mainly plants of wet places, either growing in water in the tropics *(Nymphoides)* or in wet or swampy places in the South West *(Villarsia),* and easily recognised by the fringed white or yellow flowers. *Centaurium* is also a native of the South West, while the two remaining genera are of lowly stature and are not commonly found.

Among the eight species of *Villarsia* the most remarkable is *V. calthifolia,* which has round or kidney-shaped leaves up to 225 mm in diameter and yellow flowers in large panicles up to 600 mm in length. This is the largest-leaved plant of the South West. It is very rare, being found only in moist spots among granite rocks on the summits of the Porongorup Range.

Centaurium australe is the local centaury-plant, an annual herb with pink tubular flowers found widely dispersed throughout the South

△ *Centaurium australe* (R.Br.) Ostf. . . . an annual herb widely distributed throughout the South West.

West and often used in an infusion for the purpose of increasing the appetite. It is closely related to the centaury-plant of Europe *(C. minus)* which is noted for its bitter, stomachic and tonic properties.

The *Gentianaceae* are usually recognisable by their opposite leaves, five-partite flowers with the corolla tubular in the greater and lower part, the five stamens opposite the petal-like lobes, and the one-chambered ovary with its small and numerous seeds attached to the wall of the chamber in two rows.

△ *Alyxia buxifolia* R.Br., here photographed at Point Peron, near Perth, also occurs widely far inland.

APOCYNACEAE

Oleander family

WITHIN the tropics the Oleander family is a large and important one, embracing about 300 genera and 1,300 species. The frangipani, oleander, periwinkle, Natal plum and wintersweet are familiar as horticultural subjects, and the family also contains a number of plants valuable for their drug properties, beside many which are poisonous.

Only six genera of eight species are indigenous to Western Australia and these are mostly of tropical habitat. Two of these, *Alstonia actinophylla* and *Alyxia buxifolia* have local or native uses.

Of *Alstonia actinophylla* it can be said that this is the fever-bark of Kimberley. It is related to a species already regarded as valuable in Queensland and New South Wales.

Alyxia buxifolia is the sole representative of the family in the temperate zone of Western Australia. Sometimes known as camel-bush, it is also called the dysentery-bush because of its local use as a cure for this ill, and it appears to contain substances of value in other directions. It has a wide range in the southern areas, extending from the coast to the Kalgoorlie district, northwards to the Murchison River and along the south coast eastwards to beyond Esperance. It is a densely branched and foliaged shrub three metres in height and the wood is soft and yellow—not unlike that of box *(Buxus)* from which rulers are made, and its leaves are not unlike the common European box *(B. sempervirens),* hence its specific name. The small white flowers are succeeded by red berries the size of a small pea, sometimes solitary but occasionally three or four are found like a string of small beads, one above the other. It flowers in September and October and prefers loamy soil in the interior, but the coastal forms are found in limestone or granite country. Another south western species *(Lyonsia diaphanophlebia)* is a climbing plant which grows along the lower reaches of the Murray River but this is very rare.

◁ The berries of *Alyxia buxifolia,* known as dysentery or camel bush, sometimes grow like stringed beads.

117

VERBENACEAE

Verbena family

THE flora of the interior of temperate Western Australia would be much poorer were it not for the many remarkable plants of the Verbena family which have adapted themselves to the hostile, arid area. Thriving as they do in sand and flowering late in spring, they combine remarkable qualities of foliage (usually resorting to a dense felting of the leaves and calyces) with large and frequently delicate blossoms—which stand in marked contrast to their own foliage and the texture of that of their neighbours.

The *Verbenaceae* comprises some 98 genera and some 260 species mainly tropical, of which 12 genera and 70 species are indigenous to Western Australia. Familiar examples of the family are the species of lantana, the lemon-scented verbena

△ *Lachnostachys vebascifolia* F.Muell. shows clearly remarkable adaption to cope with arid surroundings.

and the garden species of the genus *Verbena* and *Duranta,* but it is a very different type of plant that is so prominent in the sandy soils of the interior, and a whole section of *Verbenaceae* (with species not found outside Australia) make it of such local interest.

It is extraordinary that, of this galaxy of form and colour, not one plant has a distinctive common name. One group of densely felted or woolly shrubs has the common appellation of lambs' tails; this includes the species of *Lachnostachys, Newcastelia, Physopsis, Mallophora* and *Dicrastylis,* all of which have small flowers scarcely exceeding the densely woolly calyx, and all have symmetrical (regular) flowers. They grow in sand (usually in red sand) and are widely dispersed through the dry country. Most people overlook the corolla because it is the globular, woolly calyces, massed into spikes or heads, that form the attractive feature of the plant.

Other genera worthy of attention include *Pityrodia, Hemiphora, Chloanthes* and *Cyanostegia.*

◁ *Newcastelia hexarrhena* F.Muell. grows in the desert. The dense white wool is a defence against the heat.

△ *Lachnostachys eriobotrya* (F.Muell.) Druce.
. . . has densely felted calyces.

Lachnostachys, with 10 species, has violet flowers, and none of the species has a wide distribution—in fact, some of them are restricted to small areas mainly eastwards from Merredin and southwards from the Mount Magnet district. *L. vebascifolia* is found in the South West in sandy soils in but a few places but particularly in the Moora and Bakers Hill districts. *L. brevispicata* is confined to the red sandy soils of the Menzies district. Both of these last named flower in September and October.

Extending into Central Australia, six of the nine local species of *Newcastelia* are from the desert country and the other three are to be found in the districts northwards from Kalgoorlie. One of these is *N. insignis* with small lilac or white flowers, and the flowering stems and densely crowded calyces are closely woolly with golden hairs. *N. hexarrhena* occurs in desert country north-east of Kalgoorlie and in the region around Queen Victoria Spring. *N. viscida* is confined to the Comet Vale-Menzies district and grows on stony soil.

△ Woolly-foxglove *Pityrodia terminalis* (Endl.) A. S. George . . .
▽ among the most showy of all the native plants.

◁ *Lachnostachys eriobotrya* (F.Muell.) Druce . . . thriving in the sand and inland heat.

119

VERBENA FAMILY

△ *Cyanostegia angustifolia* Turcz. . . . purple-violet flowers, yellow anthers, pale violet calyx.

Physopsis spicata is one of the rare species of the South West, growing in the vicinity of the Hill River and again near York. The small yellow flowers appear in November but the white globular calyces remain on the plant for many months afterwards. *Mallophora globiflora* is a small shrub, not unlike a small cauliflower, with densely packed white flowers, and the species of *Dicrastylis* are also white or yellow, some of them being a feature of the flora of the Moora district.

The genus *Pityrodia* with 22 species, has quite different flowers. These are tubular, curved, and more or less two-lipped, not unlike those of the foxglove. Some of these, especially *P. terminalis* are among the finest and most showy of all our native plants, and are usually found in sand, flowering late in spring. It well deserves the name of woolly-foxglove. There are, however, still finer species of this genus which are not found near the main roads; a group found between Northampton and the Murchison River, which includes *P. atriplicina* and *P. oldfieldii,* would be an ornament in any garden. *P. verbascina* from the same district sometimes assumes a golden hue in its foliage, especially the younger parts of the plant. Other species have dull, felted leaves, some with flowers almost 50 mm in length. *P. bartlingii* grows further south, being common between the Arrowsmith and Murray rivers. It attains a height of more than a metre and its curious, tubercled foliage is surmounted by large, pale violet blossoms.

△ *Pityrodia oldfieldii* (F.Muell.) Benth. . . . found between Northampton and the Murchison River.

Among the more attractive plants of the family is *Hemiphora elderi* which occurs westwards from Menzies. This plant employs the dense vestiture of the lambs' tails group, with the oblique flowers of *Pityrodia.* The thick, grey, felted leaves are surmounted by spike-like racemes of large curved flowers covered with a long, loose wool of vivid crimson.

Chloanthes coccinea is not uncommon in the swampy soils around Cannington and northwards to the Arrowsmith River, but it is found in similar situations almost to the vicinity of King George Sound. It, too, has tubercled leaves and elongated racemes of scarlet curved flowers.

Woolly-dragon *Pityrodia bartlingii* (Lehm.) Benth. ▷
. . . curious foliage surmounted by large blossoms.

△ *Cyanostegia angustifolia* Turcz. . . . masses of blossoms on the roadside in spring and early summer.

Finally, mention must be made of the genus *Cyanostegia* with four species, which are so remarkable that they attract the attention of every passer-by. The roadsides between Wongan Hills and Mullewa in spring and early summer are bright with the dense pyramidal masses of the blossoms of *C. angustifolia* and the same applies to the Eastern Goldfields. The plants grow in gravelly soil, rarely exceed a metre in height, and the flowers are of a deep purple-violet with large, deep yellow anthers. Each corolla is subtended by a papery disc-like calyx of a pale violet and elegantly veined. These calyces remain long after the corollas have fallen, and then, late in summer and much faded, they are blown away by the wind. *C. lanceolata,* found eastwards from Pingelly and in the Coorow district, has much larger leaves and flowers, while *C. microphylla* of the Coolgardie district has very small, viscid leaves. The largest-flowered species of all is *C. bunnyana* of the Roebuck Bay district; in this the calyx is about the size of 10 cents, is of much firmer texture than the others, and is of a rich metallic violet. No mention has been made of those species which have silvery scales on their foliage, or of those which (like *P. teckiana* from the granite rocks of the Avon district) have no vestiture but instead have viscid foliage.

In general this family is one of the most interesting of the Western Australian flora which has its species restricted to the drier parts of the State, and no group of plants possesses such variation in form, colour and the vestiture of its flowers.

LABIATAE

Mint family

O F the 3,200 or so species of the Mint family, arranged under about 200 genera, some are valued because of their use as condiments— thyme *(Thymus)*, basil *(Ocimum)*, marjoram *(Origanum)* and sage *(Salvia)*. Others such as rosemary *(Rosmarinus)*, lavender *(Lavandula)* and peppermint *(Mentha)* yield essential oils and perfumes, while others again, such as Lion's ear *(Leonotus)*, and the shell plant *(Molucella)* are common as garden plants.

The genera native to Western Australia number 14, of which seven are restricted to the tropical north. The remaining seven—*Prostanthera, Hemigenia, Hemiandra, Wrixonia, Microcorys, Westringia* and *Teucrium*—are indigenous to the South West or the arid interior, and it is among these, especially when growing in sandy or stony places, that are to be found the most attractive examples.

Among such are the species of *Prostanthera* in which the calyx is two-lipped, often enlarging after flowering. *P. magnifica* is the finest, a shrub frequently over two metres high, with large racemes of lilac or red flowers in which the much enlarged calyx (as large as the corolla) is a deep purple or magenta in colour. *P. eckersleyana* is also a delightful shrub, seldom taller than 450 mm, with blue or violet flowers and attractive

▽ *Hemigenia incana* (Lindl.) Benth. . . . Velvety Hemigenia grows in the South West, flowers from August to February.

△ *Prostanthera magnifica* C.A.Gardn. . . . a shrub which frequently grows more than two metres high.

△ *Prostanthera eckersleyana* F.Muell. . . . a species which flourishes in the arid interior.

△ Snake bush *Hemiandra pungens* R.Br. is found on the coastal sand plains from the Murchison to Albany.

△ *Hemiandra pungens* R.Br. *var. hispida* Benth. . . . has leaves densely covered with short stiff hairs.

crinkly and toothed foliage. The remaining species are much less attractive and have white or red flowers.

The genus *Hemigenia* is probably the next in importance by reason of its blossoms. *H. macrantha* from the red sand of the northern plains has large bright red flowers which contrast with the sage-coloured foliage. *H. macphersonii* is also a distinctive species with large red blossoms, but *H. dielsii* has masses of white flowers and is a common shrub between Merredin and Kalgoorlie.

Hemiandra boasts a number of species with flowers ranging from deep violet to red or white. All these have pungent-pointed leaves nerved from the base upwards, and *H. pungens,* from which some five species can be separated, is the snake bush, common in the sand of the coastal plains between the Murchison River and King George Sound.

The low, bushy shrub *Wrixonia prostantheroides* is very attractive, its small densely crowded white or pale pink flowers being spotted with purple. It inhabits the red sand of the lower Murchison district and is the single species of this genus. Species of *Microcorys* (which have much the same general appearance as the species of *Hemigenia,* to which they are closely related) are all small shrubs and most of them inhabit the sandy or stony areas of the sandplains near the south coast. In some the flowers are crowded into heads, and in all there is that abundance of flowers which makes them desirable as garden plants.

The species of *Westringia* have white flowers in heads at the ends of the branches, and the leaves are in whorls of from three to six. They have something of the appearance of the common rosemary, and the commonest species *(W. rigida)* is equally at home at the seaside as in the arid interior. *W. discipulorum* is quite unlike the other four species, having grey hoary leaves. It is found only around Yorkrakine.

Finally mention should be made of the species of *Teucrium,* seven in number, all very unlike in appearance, but all with characteristically hooded white or yellow flowers. Rarely does one find a plant generally distributed, and most are at home in low-lying silty, often salt soils.

SOLANACEAE

Potato family

BECAUSE the floral characteristics of the *Solanaceae* are not very easily recognisable, consideration of the plants that make up the family will give a general impression of its compass. The potato *(Solanum tuberosum)*, the tomato *(Lycopersicum esculentum)*, the chillies (species of *Capsicum)*, the cape gooseberry *(Physalis peruviana)*—which is not, by the way a native of South Africa—the tobacco plant *(Nicotiana tabacum)*; among garden plants, species of *Petunia, Cestrum, Iochroma, Nierembergia, Salpiglossis* and *Schizanthus;* and of poisonous plants, belladonna *(Atropa belladonna)*, henbane *(Hyoscyamus)*, the thorn apple *(Datura)* and the local pituri *(Duboisia hopwoodii):* all of these are members of the Potato family, which is a large one containing about 2,200 species arranged under some 85 genera.

In Western Australia eight genera and 61 species occur naturally, the largest genus being *Solanum,* usually recognisable by the similarity of the flow-

△ *Solanum symonii* Eichler . . . violet flowers followed by purple fruits about the size of small olives.

ers to those of the potato. The black (often miscalled "the deadly") nightshade is not indigenous. Most of the *Solanum* species inhabit the summer rainfall regions of this State, and are best represented in the Ashburton and Fortescue districts.

S. symonii is a common shrub in the coastal sands, with dark green, narrow leaves and violet flowers succeeded by purple fruits about the size of a small olive. Perhaps the best known is *S. lasiophyllum* native to the north, but carried by sheep into the Midland and Eastern districts: it has felted leaves and prickly stems and calyces, and is very common between Coorow and Geraldton.

There is one native thorn apple *(Datura leichhardtii)* found in the Fortescue and Gascoyne districts. Of the tobacco plants ten species are native to Western Australia: all of them have narrow, white trumpet-shaped flowers and are widely dispersed. *Anthocercis* has yellow or white flowers, the tube of the flower usually terminating in

Solanum lasiophyllum Dun. . . . a native of the north, carried south by sheep.

△ *Solanum oldfieldii* F.Muell.

△ *Anthocercis viscosa* R.Br. . . . a highly perfumed flower frequently found in cracks on bare coastal rocks.

long narrow lobes. The commonest species, *A. littorea* of the coastal districts, is very common around Perth in the limestone areas. *Anthotroche,* with five species, has deep-purple velvety flowers. Most of the species have thick felted leaves, often yellow or grey, which form a charming contrast with the blossoms. These plants grow in sand in the drier areas.

The pituri *(Duboisia hopwoodii)* is perhaps the most virulent of all the poison plants of this State. It is a willow-like shrub with long, deep green, narrow leaves, white, bell-shaped flowers streaked with violet lines, and the fruits are small berries much sought after by birds. It has a wide range throughout the pastoral country and the desert, and its western boundary is almost exactly that which marks the eastern limits of agricultural development.

Finally, the lowly *Isandra bancroftii* also has white, violet-streaked flowers, but it is a shrub rarely exceeding 200 mm in height, with grey, velvety leaves. It is found in the Kondinin district.

△ The most virulent of all West Australian poison plants . . . the pituri *Duboisia hopwoodii* (F.Muell.) F.Muell.

125

△ *Eremophila gilesii* F.Muell. growing near Well 3A on the inland Canning stock route, 112 km north of Wiluna.

△ Another species, probably *Eremophila cuneifolia* Kraenzlin, from the Gibson Desert. Eremophila means desert-loving

MYOPORACEAE

Myoporum family

WITH few exceptions—a single species of *Bontia* found in the East Indies, a few African species of *Oftia* and a genus in tropical America—the *Myoporaceae* of five genera and 160 species is Australian in habitat, with the greater number found in the arid heart of the continent, most of them being from the country between the Murchison and the Rawlinson Range.

In the genus *Eremophila* alone, Western Australia has more than 100 species, all of which are shrubs, some of great beauty, and it is astonishing that no serious attempt has been made to introduce them into the gardens of the drier areas of the State. There is no distinctive common name for the *Eremophilas* apart from poverty bush, and this was bestowed on the plants because they are useless as browsing plants on pastoral properties. The name *Eremophila,* however, was given to the genus by Robert Brown in 1810. He visited these shores with Flinders, and although he did not journey into the interior, it is remarkable that he should have selected such an appropriate name, for it means 'desert loving.'

Few plants of the interior are more attractive. Some plants such as *E. fraseri,* have relatively large, dark green leaves covered with a viscous lacquer-like substance which protects the leaves from the drying influence of wind; the necessary breathing is made possible through a restricted number of breathing-pores which are found in pillar-like outgrowths (from the leaf) which protrude above the viscous layer. Other plants are remarkable for their dense covering of wool (e.g. *E. mackinlayi),* or of much branched and interlocked hairs, while others have a coating of scales over the leaves and flowers like that found in salt-bushes.

The shape of the *Eremophila* flower is tubular. This may be short, straight and inflated with short lobes, or it may be long and curved with more acute divisions. In others (e.g. *E. maculata)* the corolla has its lowest division or lobe much more deeply separated than the others.

◁ This *Eremophila* was photographed in the Kimberleys. Details are insufficient to establish the species.

△ *Eremophila oldfieldii* F.Muell.

△ *Eremophila decipiens* Ostf.

△ *Eremophila viscida* Endl. . . . a lacquer-like covering to protect its leaves from the drying winds.

△ *Eremophila glabra* (R.Br.) Ostf. . . leaves with pillar-like breathing pores.

Native fuchsia *Eremophila maculata* F.Muell. . . . grows ▷ in low-lying clay soil in Gascoyne and Murchison areas.

△ *Eremophila pantoni* F.Muell.

△ *Eremophila punicia* S.Moore. . . . a dense wool covering.

The colour of the flower varies from violet to white with yellow, red and purple-flowered species, and a number are spotted with brown or purple in the throat of the tube. The stamens are four in number, and the free ovary, placed above the base of the corolla, usually has a long slender style. The two anther-cells are almost free from each other and united at the top only—one of the main characteristics separating these plants from the family *Verbenaceae* with which the *Myoporaceae* has close affinities.

A characteristic of many of the species is that the calyx, after flowering, becomes enlarged, the sepals taking on the appearance of petals, and some of the species are more attractive in fruit than they are when in blossom. The reason for this cannot be readily explained, since this takes place after, and not before, fertilisation of the ovule, hence it serves no useful purpose in this respect.

Eremophila mackinlayi is typical of the species which have a densely woolly calyx not enlarging after flowering. It is found from Shark Bay to Cue and Yalgoo, and is a shrub from one to 2.5 metres high, and highly attractive when in flower. *E. maculata* is called the native fuchsia. Not in the least resembling a fuchsia, this species is found in low-lying spots in clay soil subject to flooding, and thus on the plains adjoining watercourses. It has a wide range through the Gascoyne and Murchison districts.

E. platycalyx represents those species in which the calyx enlarges after flowering. The corolla is not highly coloured, but a dull red and spotted with brown. It is a common species throughout the mulga country. *E. clarkei* is a shrub from 1.2 to 1.8 metres high, with narrow leaves, growing in stony soil on rises and is common in the western areas of the mulga country.

Apart from the genus *Eremophila,* the family is represented in Western Australia by the species of *Myoporum* which are shrubs or small trees with small regular white flowers. Most of them are found close to the sea, but some extend inland, especially on the Nullarbor Plain and are called dogwoods or red sandalwoods.

◁ *Myoporum parvifolium* R.Br. . . . a low-spreading shrub usually found close to the sea.

128

LOBELIACEAE

Lobelia family

USUALLY included in the Canterbury-bell family *(Campanulaceae)*, the *Lobeliaceae* differ in having irregular flowers and united anthers.

There are two genera in Western Australia—*Lobelia* and *Isotoma,* the former easily recognised by the characteristic heraldic fleur-de-lis shape of its flowers. All of the *Lobelia* are blue, and all of them have a milky sap in the stems.

Lobelia tenuior is not uncommon in the South West, especially around Perth, in sandy soil, flowering in the late spring, an annual of slender habit and flowers which range from a deep to a pale blue. Some species occur in swampy places, but the largest and most attractive are those which occur in the loamy or sandy soils of the dry interior, especially in the mulga country.

Isotoma, a genus with five local species, contains slender dwarf herbs with small succulent foliage, or the more robust *I. hypocrateriformis,* common in many places in the South West and extending about 200 miles inland. There are two forms, the normal form as illustrated below, and a smaller form with pale purple-violet flowers. Both are patterned with deep reddish-purple marks, and have a copious milky juice.

A characteristic of the dry country species of the family is their succulent nature. Annuals of comparatively short duration, they flower and fruit during hot dry weather, utilising the sap stored in stems and leaves. That of the leaves is used up first, and then the stems wither from the base upwards, the final apical moisture being responsible for the last seed-vessel.

△ *Lobelia tenuior* R.Br. . . . its flowers have a characteristic heraldic fleur-de-lis shape.

△ The smaller *Isotoma hypocrateriformis* (R.Br.) Druce.

◁ The more common form of *Isotoma hypocrateriformis.*

129

GOODENIACEAE

Leschenaultia family

MAINLY Australian in its distribution, the Leschenaultia family comprises 13 genera and more than 300 species, and of these all the genera and 205 species occur in Western Australia.

Some of the most attractive of our native plants belong to the *Goodeniaceae*, particularly the species of *Lechenaultia*, *Velleia*, *Goodenia* and *Dampiera*.

Of the 18 species of *Lechenaultia*, one is tropical, and the remainder are found in the South West. Although the most popular is undoubtedly the blue-flowered *L. biloba* with blossoms which range in colour from pure white to a deep ultramarine, there are other species quite as attractive if not more so than this. The flowers range from a rich scarlet to orange, yellow, blue and violet, while one is a deep green with small intense blue teeth at the top of the tube.

The common blue leschenaultia *(L. biloba)* is too well known to need any description. It is the most familar of the six blue-flowered species, and has a wide range; the deepest blue flowers are usually found in gravelly clay, and the pure white forms in deep sand in the drier areas.

There are five red-flowered species, three of which deserve mention: the commonest is *L. formosa* which is common in the areas southwards from Wagin, but it also occurs sparingly in the Midlands areas. This plant is very diffuse or almost prostrate, and flowers in September, the

△ Blue leschenaultia and banjine *Pimelea spectabilis* (Fisch. et. Mey.) Lindl. in the Darling Range.

▽ Below, left and right: The common blue *Lechenaultia biloba* Lindl.

shrubs often being as much as 600 mm in diameter. *L. hirsuta* is a most arresting species when in flower. When erect it is as much as 450 mm tall, but it is usually of wiry spreading habit, with little foliage, the stems and leaves being glandular-hairy. The flowers are an intense scarlet, of a hue rarely seen in flowering plants, and, growing in the Midlands districts, it flowers from September until January in loose white sand. Another red-flowered species is *L. laricina* which was formerly common in the Meenaar district, but is now almost extinct. Something like *L. formosa,* the stems are more erect, and the crowded leaves and flowers give it a distinctive appearance.

Among the yellow-flowered species are two which are sometimes suffused with an orange-red. The finest of these, and the largest flowered species of the genus is *L. macrantha,* which has the mat-like habit of *L. formosa* but it always flowers peripherally, so that the flowering plant has the appearance of a wreath with a leafy centre. Plants as much as 750 mm in diameter are not rare, yet they seldom exceed 100 mm in height. It appears to be the only herbaceous species, losing its leafy stem during the summer. The other is *L. linarioides* which is a shrub up to a metre in height, with masses of yellow flowers, commonly suffused with a brick red. Mainly at home in the limestone tracts of the west coast between the Murchison and Swan rivers, and formerly common in the districts near Perth, it extends inland on sand heaths to Watheroo, Mingenew and Mullewa.

Then there is *L. superba,* a lovely small plant with large orange-coloured flowers which is very

△ *Lechenaultia linarioides* D.C., a shrub to a metre high which grows between the Murchison and Swan rivers.

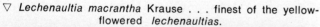

▽ *Lechenaultia macrantha* Krause . . . finest of the yellow-flowered *lechenaultias.*

rare, and only found in stony places near the south coast.

L. tubiflora, common in white sand between the Moore River and the Wagin district, has red tubular flowers arising from densely leafy stems rarely exceeding four inches in height. The almost total absence of wings to the corolla make it a very distinctive species. Also to be found near the south coast is *L. acutiloba,* which closely resembles *L. tubiflora* in the absence of expanded corolla wings, but the flowers are green or yellow, with intense deep blue or purple lobes.

Of the remainder few are worthy of particular mention except, perhaps, *L. helmsii* a tall blue-flowered species often three or four feet in height, which grows in the red sand dunes to the north of Kalgoorlie, and the violet-flowered *L. agrostophylla* of Kimberley which grows on the low-lying grassy plains.

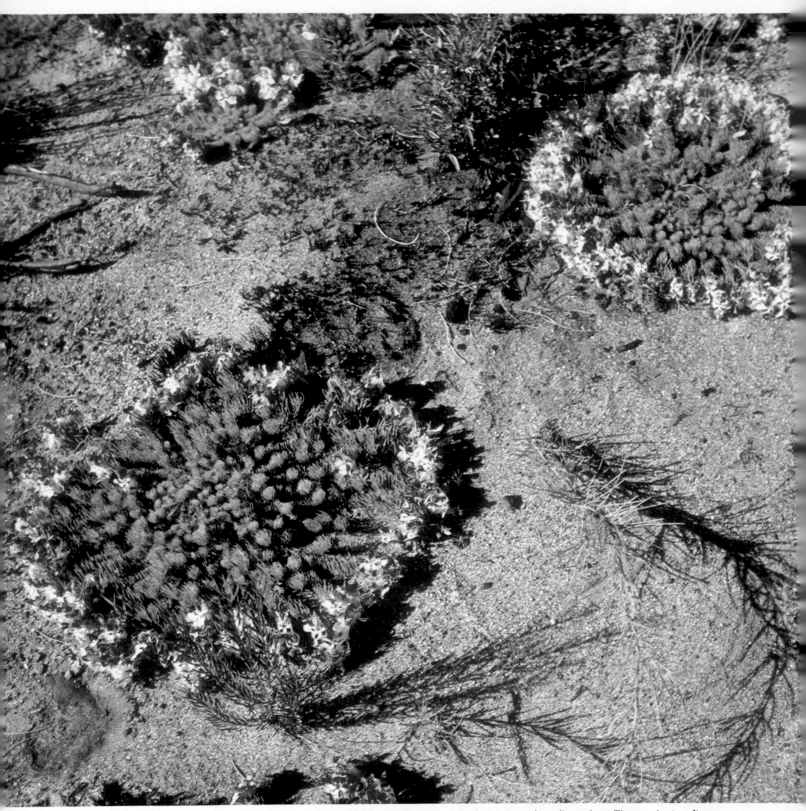

△ *Lechenaultia macrantha* Krause . . . looks like a wreath with a leafy centre when flowering. These plants often reach 750 mm in diameter, but rarely exceed 100 mm in height.

LESCHENAULTIA FAMILY

The genus *Goodenia* provides some very attractive species, especially the low and compact *G. primulacea* which, indeed, except for its irregular flowers, looks like a primrose. This dwarf grows in the yellow sand of the Eastern districts and the Goldfields, flowering late in the year. *G. pinnatifida* is a large-flowered yellow-blossomed plant with a wide range in the mulga country, often occurring gregariously. Large blue—or purple—flowered species of the desert interior such as *G. dyeri* and *G. stapfiana* provide some the finest flowers of the red sand tracts of the interior.

Dampiera, with 50 species in Western Australia, has, as a rule, flowers of a particular shade of dusty ultramarine of the same shape and form as those of *Lechenaultia,* but the two small "ears" on the two upper (smaller) corolla lobes are deeply concave, usually a deep purple within, and enclose the *indusium* when the flower is in bud— a characteristic feature of this genus. The name commemorates William Dampier who collected the first species *(D. incana)* and who remarked on the prevalence of blue in the flora of New Holland. The calyx lobes are very minute, the calyx usually grey-hoary. Although this dusky blue characterises the majority of the species, *D. luteiflora* is a notable exception. This attractive plant is common in the yellow sand of the heathlands of the Eastern Goldfields eastwards from Southern Cross, flowering in November.

Two equally attractive blue-flowered species are *D. wellsiana* and *D. eriocephala* which are characterised by having dense, almost head-like clusters of flowers which may expand before they ripen their seed. *D. wellsiana* has broad basal tufted leaves devoid of hairs, and grows in the Eastern districts under the same conditions as, and often with *D. luteiflora,* while *D. eriocephala* is only found in the South West, from Tammin to the Stirling Range, and is more frequently met with among the hills, or in ironstone gravel.

△ *Dampiera wellsiana* F.Muell. . . . common in the Eastern Goldfields, ▽ often seen with yellow *Dampiera luteiflora.*

△ *Dampiera wellsiana* F.Muell.

◁ *Dampiera diversifolia* De Vr.

LESCHENAULTIA FAMILY

V. rosea
9/2 ♂ ♀ ♂
muellevi

△ *Scaevola nitida* R.Br. . . . a common shrub of the coastal sand dunes.

△ *Dampiera linearis* R.Br. . . . narrow-leaved *Dampiera.*

△ *Velleia trinervis* Labill. . . . grows widely in the south-west corner of the State.

Mention should be made of the genus *Anthotium* which includes some charming species, especially *A. rubriflorum,* a small tufted plant reminiscent of a thrift, but with head-like clusters of flowers of an intense red. It is common in the Meckering district (or was formerly) and may be found as far north as Bencubbin, in gravelly soil, flowering late in the year. When occurring with *Dampiera wellsiana,* which it frequently does, the remarkable contrast of rich red and blue by these two small, tufted plants is really attractive.

The genus *Calogyne* is distinguished by the presence of a branched style, the two or three branches each terminating in the cup-shaped *indusium* and bearing a resemblance to a candelabrum. The flowers of *C. berardiana,* widely distributed, but most common in the districts around Geraldton, might be mistaken for a yellow-flowered species of *Goodenia,* and are thus often overlooked.

Goodenia eatoniana F.Muell.

△ *Dampiera teres* Lindl. growing beside the Moora-Mogumber road near Mogumber.

△ *Scaevola glandulifera* D.C.

△ *Scaevola platyphylla* Lindl.

△ *Scaevola striata* R.Br. . . . in the Darling Range.

▽ *Velleia discophora* F.Muell.

Plants of the family with pure white flowers are not common, but *Diaspasis filifolia* is one, and this occurs gregariously in swampy places near King George Sound, flowering almost throughout the summer.

Scaevola is another large genus in the Western Australian flora, and some of the flowers are large and brilliantly coloured, e.g. the prostrate *S. phlebopetala* which is common in white sand, and flowers throughout the summer, and the tall *S. striata,* a common species of the gravelly soil of the Darling Range as far north as the Moore River. *Scaevola crassifolia* is a common shrub of the coastal sand dunes. Found between Geraldton and Esperance it grows to a height of nearly a metre and has leathery leaves.

The flowers of this family are irregular, the corolla-lobes being winged, or at least the three lower, and it is these wings which make up the most attractive part of the flower.

The ovary in the family is situated below the corolla, and the most distinctive feature is the *indusium,* a cup-shaped organ which surrounds and encloses the stigma. It is a pollen-receiving cup which performs a necessary function in securing cross-pollination, and a feature which indicates a very advanced development in the family's status. This *indusium* is characteristic also of the blue-pincushion flower *(Brunonia)* which is usually placed in a distinct family because of its superior ovary.

STYLIDIACEAE

Trigger-plant family

△ *Stylidium schoenoides* D.C. . . . intriguing trigger mechanism for fertilisation of the species.

BELONGING to a different division of the vegetable kingdom, the Trigger-plant family is nevertheless almost analogous with the Orchid family. This is due to the union in *Stylidiaceae* of the male and female organs into one structure which (in the Australian genera) terminates in a stigma situated between two anthers.

The Trigger-plants are confined to the southern hemisphere and, of the six genera, two—*Levenhookia* and *Stylidium*—are found in Western Australia. Seven out of a total of eight species of *Levenhookia* are indigenous to the South West, while of the family's total of 136 species, 111 of these are widely dispersed in this State.

The mechanism by which fertilisation of these plants takes place is most intriguing. Like the orchids, the trigger plants have a labellum or lip, and this, in *Stylidium,* is very small, its function being apparently to form a landing place for visiting insects. When this occurs, a stimulus is immediately imparted to the long elastic column which, lying in a reflexed position at the "ready," immediately descends with a hammer-like action, shedding pollen on to a visitor, and receiving on its stigma (if receptive) pollen from another flower of the same species brought by the visiting insect. The rapid action of this column or "trigger" is quite remarkable and well worthy of investigation, but it should be noted that a time must elapse between two successive trigger actions, which varies with the day and the species.

△ ▽ *Stylidium bulbiferum* Benth.

The species of *Levenhookia* are dwarf annuals found mainly in wet areas, although one of the finest of the species occurs in dry sandy country in the Murchison, where in places it carpets the ground in October.

The species of *Stylidium* vary from dwarf annuals to shrubs and a number are climbing plants; they fall into easily recognisable groups according to their habit of growth, whether climbers, shrubs, or herbs, and according to their leaf arrangement. *S. brunonianum* is a common example

△ *Stylidium crossocephalum* F.Muell.

▽ *Stylidium elongatum* Benth.

△ *Stylidium brunonianum* Benth. . . . a common example.

▽ *Stylidium calcaratum* R.Br.

TRIGGER-PLANT FAMILY

of those species which have a basal rosette of densely crowded leaves, and the scapes or stems above bear, at intervals, whorls of leaf-like bracts. The flowers of this species are pink or pale violet, and the plant is not uncommon, growing in sand in the Perth district, and extending northwards to the Murchison and southwards to the Murray River. *S. elongatum* is an example of those species which are perennial and have long grass-like leaves and elongated panicles of pink flowers. It is common in the Geraldton and Northampton districts, extending eastwards to Indarra. *S. scandens* is one of the climbing plants and is common between King George Sound and the Stirling Range, inhabiting damp shady spots. The flowers are rose-pink, and the elongated wiry stems carry whorls of narrow leaves, with tendril-like points by which the plants support themselves, often growing to a height of five feet. *S. affine* represents still another type with long grass-like leaves, but intermixed with long narrow transparent scales, and the flowers are in very short racemes.

△ *Stylidium junceum* R.Br.

△ *Stylidium schoenoides* D.C. . . . long grass-like leaves.

COMPOSITAE

Daisy family

PROBABLY no other land can boast such a richness of everlastings as Western Australia, and these are but some of the members of the Daisy family indigenous to this State.

This family, the *Compositae,* is one of the largest of all flowering plants and consists of over 20,000 species, grouped under about 1,000 genera, and found in almost every quarter of the globe.

Two hundred and forty two species in 68 genera can be claimed as native to Western Australia, but a large number of naturalised aliens which rank as weeds would make the total much larger.

A few of the plants are shrubs, such as species of *Olearia,* but by far the greater number are annual herbs which vary from the tiny earth-heads *(Chthonocephalus)* to the splendid everlastings which decorate, and are such a feature of the mulga-country, where in a good season they carpet the ground over large tracts with their bright pinks and yellows, intermixed with white.

What is popularly called a "flower" in the daisy family is in reality a cluster, spike or head of densely compacted florets (little flowers) which, in the familiar daisy or marguerite, consists of a button-like centre or boss of perfect bisexual florets, surrounded by the petal-like flowers of the ray, usually female or neuter.

In the everlastings such as *Helichrysum, Helipterum* and *Waitzia,* the outer ray-flowers are wanting, and their place is taken by coloured chaffy bracts of which the innermost are petal-like, and the outermost smaller and frequently brown or transparent.

In another group, typified by *Cephalipterum drummondii,* the flower—or strictly, the compound head—consists of a large number of separate heads crowded on a single receptacle, the result being a ball-like structure, each partial head being surrounded by bracts which in this case are either yellow or white.

Helipterum and *Helichrysum,* together with *Schoenia,* make up by far the greatest number of everlastings. The largest of all is *Helipterum*

On the Coastal Highway south of Carnarvon, pink *Schoenia cassiniana* (Gaud.) Steetz and yellow *Cephalipterum drummondii* A. Gray. ▷

◁ Yellow everlastings *Cephalipterum drummondii* A. Gray flank Great Northern Highway south of Paynes Find.

△ In the mulga country everlastings may carpet the low-lying plains for many kilometres like freshly

▽ *Schoenia cassiniana* (Gaud.) Steetz . . . a common everlasting.

8/30 McqMoora

splendidum: it has wiry stems up to 450 mm tall, very few narrow succulent leaves, and large white daisy-like solitary heads often 50 mm in diameter; some of the innermost bracts each have a black spot at the base. In places in the mulga country these plants carpet the low-lying plains for miles like freshly fallen snow. *Schoenia cassiniana* is almost equally common and has a wider range, extending into the South West. *Helichrysum davenportii* is another common and gregarious species (often growing with *Helipterum splendidum*). The flower-heads are a rich rose-pink and solitary on long stalks from a basal tuft of rather broad leaves. The species when in seed is almost as attractive because of its long plumed bristles which form a downy, globular head. In the South West *Helichrysum roseum* and *Helipterum manglesii* are the two common pink-flowered species, the former like a common daisy with spreading, inner, petal-like bracts, the latter with drooping, pale pink heads, with the outermost bracts often grey.

llen snow. *Helipterum tenellum* Turcz. forms this carpet near Leonora beside the road from Wiluna.

▽ *Helichrysum lindleyi* Eichler growing beside the Mingenew-Three Springs road.

DAISY FAMILY

Helichrysum bracteatum is a well known garden subject, already widely cultivated in Europe as the "immortelle" before 1850. It is common amongst granite rocks in the South West where it attains to a height of a metre, with large flower-heads often 50 mm in diameter, and bracts of a rich yellow, often suffused with a bronze-like tint. The variety *albidum* has white or rarely rose-tinted bracts, and is usually a smaller plant than the typical yellow-flowered form. This is restricted to the South West and grows in limestone country.

Cephalipterum drummondii is almost equally a yellow or a white-flowered species. Its large compound globular heads, often nearly 50 mm in diameter, are common in the mulga country where white appears to predominate, while nearer the coast in the Geraldton district yellow is equally common. It flowers in the spring like all the other annual Asteraceae.

Olearia rudis is perhaps the most attractive species of this genus of shrubby plants. It has a characteristic daisy flower-head, with ray florets of a pale violet, much resembling the common Michaelmas daisies grown in gardens. A shrub a metre tall, it is common in the limestone country of the South West, but extends inland to the stony hills of the Stirling Range, and flowers in late spring.

Podolepis gracilis is a summer flowering annual 300 to 600 mm tall with wiry branched stems and pale-lilac or rose-pink rays. It is common a few kilometres northwards from Perth, in low-lying sandy soils.

△ *Helichrysum bracteatum* (Vent.) Andr., from the South West, now commonly cultivated in Europe. ▽

△ *Helichrysum bracteatum* (Vent.) Andr.

△ *Olearia rudis* (Benth.) F.Muell. . . . common in the limestone country of the South West.

△ *Brachycome iberidifolia* Benth.

△ *Waitzia acuminata* Steetz. 8130

▽ *Podolepis gracilis* Grah.

△ *Podolepis canescens* A. Cunn. ex D.C.

▽ *Helipterum cotula* (Benth.) D.C.

Flower carpets in the West Australian countryside are not confined to everlastings. Other species, given the right conditions, for
Here *Velleia rosea* S. Moore, of the Leschenaultia family, carpets the bush near Paynes Fin

rpets just as thick, but usually they are not as extensive because the everlastings can adapt themselves better to varied soils. *cacia grasbyi* Maiden (left) and *Acacia craspedocarpa* F.Muell. provide the "mulga" brush coverage.

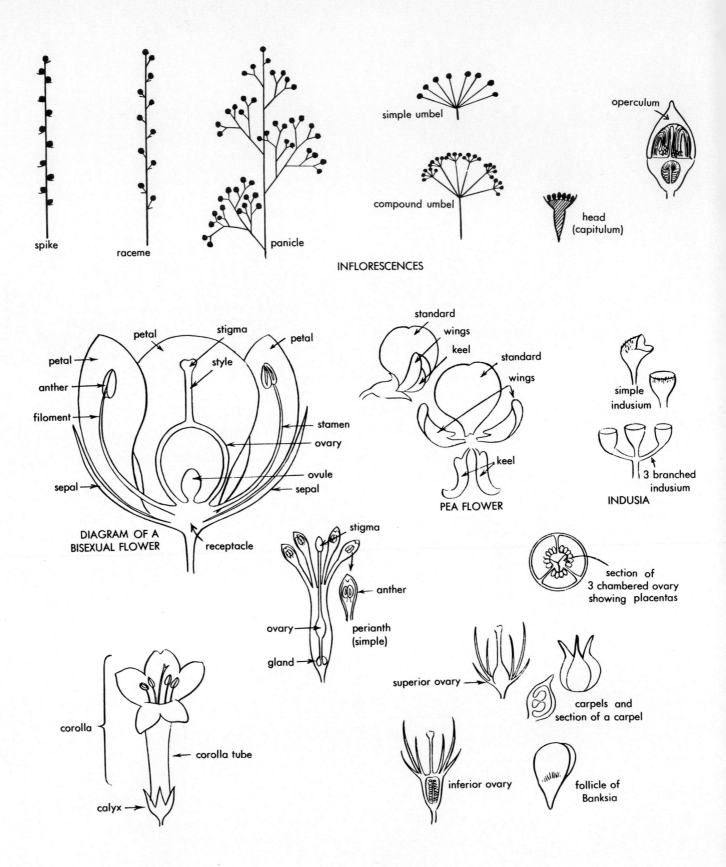

spike

raceme

panicle

simple umbel

compound umbel

head
(capitulum)

operculum

INFLORESCENCES

petal

petal

stigma

style

petal

anther

stamen

filoment

ovary

ovule

sepal

sepal

DIAGRAM OF A
BISEXUAL FLOWER

receptacle

standard

wings

keel

standard

wings

keel

PEA FLOWER

simple
indusium

3 branched
indusium

INDUSIA

stigma

anther

ovary

perianth
(simple)

gland

section of
3 chambered ovary
showing placentas

corolla

corolla tube

calyx

superior ovary

carpels and
section of a carpel

inferior ovary

follicle of
Banksia

GLOSSARY

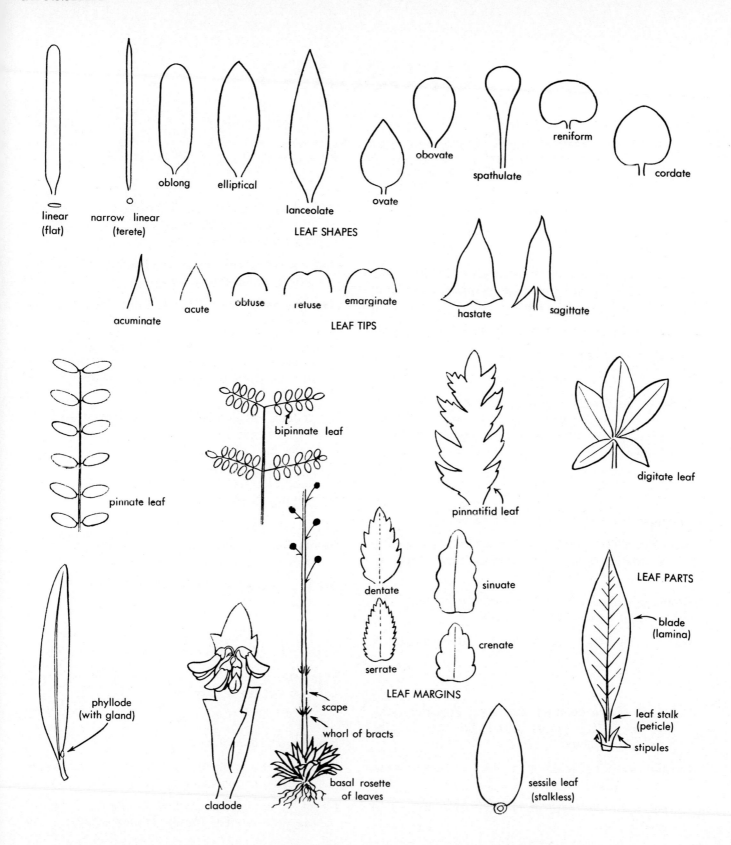

linear (flat)

narrow linear (terete)

oblong

elliptical

lanceolate

ovate

obovate

spathulate

reniform

cordate

LEAF SHAPES

acuminate

acute

obtuse

retuse

emarginate

hastate

sagittate

LEAF TIPS

bipinnate leaf

pinnatifid leaf

digitate leaf

pinnate leaf

dentate

sinuate

serrate

crenate

LEAF MARGINS

phyllode (with gland)

cladode

scape

whorl of bracts

basal rosette of leaves

sessile leaf (stalkless)

LEAF PARTS

blade (lamina)

leaf stalk (peticle)

stipules

GLOSSARY

The following explanation of terms used in the text will be of value to the ordinary reader, and the diagrams which appear on pages 148-149 will assist further in identifying the parts of plants referred to.

A

Annual, used of plants which perish within one year.

Anther, that portion of the stamen which contains the pollen, usually of two compartments and attached to a filament.

Apex, the tip of an organ, such as a leaf or petal.

Apical, pertaining to the apex.

Awn, a bristle-like appendage.

Axis, an imaginary line around which organs are developed; the axis of an inflorescence is that part of the stem or branch upon which the flowers are borne.

B

Bilocular, of two compartments; two-celled.

Bisexual, pertaining to flowers which possess both stamens and pistil(s); possessing perfect, i.e. hermaphrodite, flowers.

Bract, modified leaves intermediate between the normal leaves and the calyx.

Bulb, a modified bud, usually underground.

C

Calyx, the outermost of the floral envelopes, external to the petals or corolla, and usually green in colour.

Carnivorous, flesh-eating; applied to those plants which digest insects.

Carpel, a simple pistil or element of a compound pistil.

Characteristics, the technical differences whereby allied forms, such as generic and specific, are distinguished.

Cladode, a branch consisting of a single internode which stimulates a leaf.

Cone, a compound fruit resembling that of a pine tree.

Corolla, the floral envelope inside the calyx, usually coloured, and which in popular language is often more especially meant by "the flower."

Cotyledons, the future seed-leaves contained within the seed; one in monocotyledons (e.g. grasses); two in dicotyledons. Monocotyledonous plants usually have parallel-veined leaves; dicotyledons have pinnately or net-veined leaves.

D

Deciduous, falling in season, as petals fall after flowering, or leaves in autumn.

Drift, an expanse of a single species growing in masses.

E

Entire (leaves), without toothing or division.

Epiphyte, a plant which grows on other plants but not as a parasite.

F

Family, a group of genera.

Filament, the stalk of an anther, the thread-like stem; any thread-like body.

Floret, a small flower which is one of a cluster, as in the daisy family **(Compositae).**

GLOSSARY

Follicle, a fruit of one carpel opening along one side.

Fronds, the foliage of ferns.

G

Genus, the smallest natural group of plants containing distinct species. (Plural, **genera.**)

Glabrous, smooth, without hairs or down.

Glandular (hairs), hairs tipped by a definite secreting structure at the apex.

H

Herbaceous, plants without woody stems.

Herbs, either annuals or perennials which have the parts above ground renewed every one, or few, years.

Host (plant), one which nourishes a parasite.

I

Indigenous, native to the country, not introduced.

Inflorescence, the disposition of the flowers on the floral axis.

Insectivorous, used of those plants which capture insects and absorb nutriment from them.

Involucre, a ring of bracts surrounding several flowers in a head or head-like cluster.

J

Jam country, that type of country in which the jam tree (**Acacia acuminata**) is predominant.

Jarrah forest, the forest region of south western Australia in which the jarrah tree (**Eucalyptus marginata**) predominates.

K

Karri forest, the forest region of the extreme south west in which the dominant tree is the karri (**Eucalyptus diversicolor**).

L

Legume, a pod-bearing plant.

Littoral, pertaining to the sea-shore; belonging to or growing near the sea.

M

Mallee (country), country in which shrubby forms of **Eucalyptus** (mallees) are common.

Mulga (country), country in which the mulga (**Acacia aneura**) and associated species of **Acacia** are dominant.

N

Nectar, a sweet fluid extruded from various parts of plants, usually from the flowers.

Nerve, a simple, or embranched, vein or slender rib.

O

Opposite (leaves), leaves which arise in pairs at the one node.

Ovary, that part of the pistil which contains the ovules.

Ovule, the young seed in the ovary; the organ which after fertilization develops into a seed.

P

Papillae, soft superficial glands or protuberances.

Parasite, a plant that lives on another plant in order to obtain some or all of its nutriment.

Perennial, plant which lasts for several years in the soil, not perishing normally after once flowering and seeding.

Perianth, the floral envelopes, or calyx, or corolla, or both.

Petal, a single organ of the corolla.

Phyllode, a petiole or leaf-stalk assuming the form and functions of a leaf.

Pinnate, with leaflets arranged on each side of a common axis or leaf-stalk.

Pistil, female organ of flower consisting of ovary, style and stigma.

Placenta, the organ which bears the ovules in an ovary.

Pungent, ending in a rigid and sharp point.

R

Ray, the marginal portion of the daisy flower as distinct from the centre or disc.

Regular (flowers), uniform or symmetrical in shape or structure.

S

Salt-pans, depressions in the ground that hold water in the wet season and in which deposits of salt are formed (salt-lakes on a diminutive scale).

Saprophyte, a plant which lives on dead organic matter.

Scale, any thin chaffy body, usually a degenerate leaf.

Segment, one of the divisions into which a plant's organs, such as a leaf, may be cleft.

Sepal, a free division of the calyx.

Species, the unit in classification, the aggregate of all those individuals which have the same constant and distinctive characters.

Spinescent, bearing spines or thorns.

Stamen, the male portion of the flower consisting of a filament bearing a pollen-bearing anther at the summit.

Standard, the outermost petal of the pea-shaped flower.

Stigma, the part of style or ovary surface that receives pollen in impregnation.

Stipule, an appendage of a leaf on each side of the base of the leaf-stalk.

Striated, streaked, marked with fine longitudinal parallel lines.

Style, the usually attenuated portion of the pistil or carpel between the ovary and the stigma.

T

Tendril, a thread-like production of the stem or leaf by which a plant may secure itself in its position.

Tube, any hollow elongated body or part of an organ, such as the united portion of the corolla below the lobes.

Tuber, a subterranean stem, swollen and provided with buds, or "eyes" such as a potato.

U

Umbel, an inflorescence in which a number of pedicels or individual flower-stalks spring from the same point.

Undershrub, a low shrub, often partially herbaceous.

V

Viscid, viscous, sticky or gummy.

W

Wandoo, the native name for the white gum (**Eucalyptus redunca var. elata**).

Whorl, the arrangement of organs in a circle round an axis.

INDEX

INDEX

INDEX

ABBREVIATIONS

Abbreviations used in captions to denote the names of botanists who first described the species are as follows:

Ait.	Aiton, W.
Alef.	Alefeld, F.
Andr.	Andrews, H. C.
Baill.	Baillon, E. H.
Bak. f.	Baker, E. G.
Bartl.	Bartling, F. G.
Benth.	Bentham, G.
Blakely	Blakely, W. F.
N.E. Br.	Brown, N. E.
R. Br.	Brown, R.
Bunge	Bunge, A. von
Chinnock	Chinnock, R. J.
D.C.	de Candolle, A. P.
A. Cunn.	Cunningham, A.
Dehn.	Dehnhardt, F.
Desf.	Desfontaines, R. L.
Diels	Diels, L.
Domin	Domin, K.
D. Don	Don, D.
G. Don	Don, G.
Donn	Donn, J.
Druce	Druce, G. C.
Drumm.	Drummond, J.
Dun.	Dunal, M. F.
Eichler	Eichler, Hj.
Endl.	Endlicher, S. L.
Fenzl	Fenzl, E.
Fisch.	Fischer, F. E. L.
W.V. Fitzg.	Fitzgerald, W. V.
N. Ford	Ford, N.
C.A. Gardn.	Gardner, C. A.
Gaud.	Gaudichaud-Beaupre, C.
Gilg	Gilg, E. F.
Giord.	Giordano, F.
Grah.	Graham, R.
A. Gray	Gray, A.
Harv.	Harvey, W. H.
Hemsl.	Hemsley, W. B.
Hochr.	Hochreutiner, B. P. G.
Hook.	Hooker, Sir W. J.
Hueg.	Huegel, Baron C. von
Jacq.	Jacquin, Baron N. J. von

Kipp.	Kippist, J.
Klotzsch	Klotzsch, J. F.
Knight	Knight, J. K.
Kraenzlin	Kraenzlin, F.
Krause	Krause, K.
L.	Linnaeus; or Linne, C. von
Labill.	Labillardiere, J. J. H. de
Lehm.	Lehmann, J. G. C.
Lindl.	Lindley, J.
Maiden	Maiden, J. H.
Meissn.	Meissner, K. F.
Mey.	Meyer, C. A.
S. Moore	Moore, S. le M.
Morris	Morris, P. F.
F. Muell.	Mueller, Baron F. von
Nees	Nees von Esenbeck, C. G.
Orchard	Orchard, A. E.
Ostf.	Ostenfeld, C. H.
Otto	Otto, F.
Preiss	Preiss, L.
E. Pritzel	Pritzel, E.
Putterl.	Putterlick, A.
Reichb. f.	Reichenbach, H. G.
A. Rich.	Richard, A.
Roth	Roth, A. W.
Schau.	Schauer, J. C.
Sims	Sims, J.
Sm.	Smith, Sir J. E.
Soland	Solander, D. C.
Sond.	Sonder, W. O.
Steedman	Steedman, H.
Steetz	Steetz, J.
Steud.	Steudal, E. T.
Stschegl.	Stschegleew, S.
Sweet	Sweet, R.
Tovey	Tovey, J. R.
Turcz.	Turczaninow, N.
Turrill	Turrill, W. B.
Vent.	Ventenat, E. P.
Vickery	Vickery, J.
De Vr.	Vriese, W. H. de
Willd.	Willdenow, C. L.